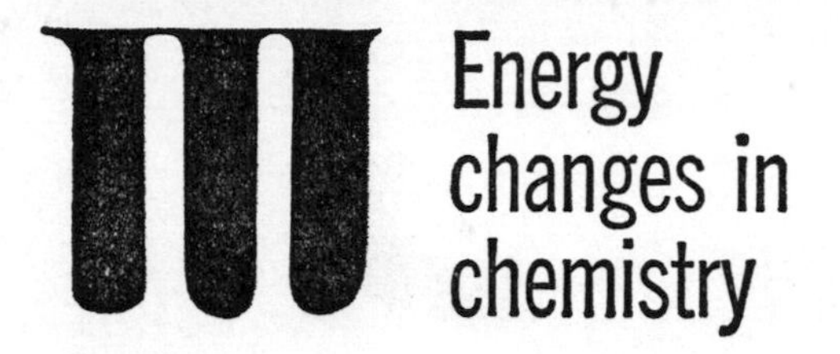

Energy changes in chemistry

Energy changes in chemistry

by J. A. Allen

Professor of Chemistry

University of Newcastle

N.S.W., Australia

London BLACKIE Glasgow

BLACKIE & SON LIMITED
5 Fitzhardinge Street
Portman Square
London, W.1
Bishopbriggs, Glasgow
BLACKIE & SON (INDIA LIMITED)
103-5 Fort Street
Bombay

Reprinted 1966 (twice) 1968

Printed by
BELL & BAIN LIMITED
Glasgow

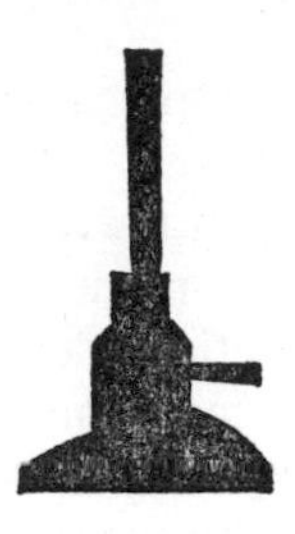

Preface

There are few topics in chemistry which present more difficulty to the student in his or her early stages than chemical thermodynamics. To many, the central problem arises from the abstract and intractable looking Second Law. Much effort is frequently expended in the formal developments leading to this law, so that when the time comes to employ the principles of thermodynamics in recognizably useful chemical problems, enthusiasm and confidence have usually evaporated, often never to return. In school courses, little more than simple applications of the First Law is customarily attempted, with the result that important basic concepts in chemistry cannot be developed in a rational manner.

One aim of this book is to attempt to alleviate this difficulty by an informal approach directed towards achieving some practical ability to predict the behaviour of chemical reactions under a variety of conditions, and to relate this behaviour to the structure and properties of the reactants and products. If such an aim is to be achieved even in part at the introductory level, it appears inevitable that many concepts dependent on the Second and Third Laws will have to be introduced without rigorous development. The approach used here is through chemical equilibria, the equilibrium constant, and its relationship to the standard free energy change for a reaction. In this respect it is the reverse of the customary formal treatment.

This is not intended as an elementary book on chemical thermodynamics, of which there are already plenty available, but seeks to initiate the possibility that energy and energy changes in chemistry may provide a useful unifying theme in the teaching of the subject. If it does little more than place in better perspective at an elementary level those things which can be observed and measured with models devised to account for or explain these observations, it will, perhaps, have served to improve the balance in the teaching of chemistry.

The stimulus for this book came initially from the annual Summer Schools for Chemistry Teachers conducted in recent years by the University of New South Wales. Its preparation has been greatly facilitated by the helpful comments and criticisms of my colleagues in the Department of Chemistry of the University of Newcastle, N.S.W. My special thanks are due to Mr. P. H. Scaife who checked the answers to the problems.

University of Newcastle,
Newcastle, N.S.W.,
Australia.
1965

Acknowledgments

The publishers gratefully acknowledge permission to use the following illustrations:

Figure 2.1 Kubaschewski and Evans, "Metallurgical Thermochemistry", 1958, Pergamon Press Ltd.

Figures 5.3–5.10 Journal of Chemical Education.

Figure 5.11 Aylward and Symes (Editors) "Approach to Chemistry", 1962, University of New South Wales Press.

Figure 6.3 Mortimer, "Reaction Heats and Bond Strengths", 1962, Pergamon Press Ltd.

Figures 7.1–7.4 Journal of Applied Chemistry.

Contents

CHAPTER

1	Equilibria and Equilibrium Constants	1
2	Equilibria and Energy	13
3	The Influence of Temperature on Equilibria	33
4	Energy Changes in Solutions	45
5	Energy Relationships in the Periodic Classification	62
6	Energy and Chemical Bonding	78
7	An Energetic Approach to a Problem in Catalysis	98
8	The Rates of Chemical Reactions	107
	Appendix—Sources of Data	117
	Answers to Problems	118
	List of Symbols	121
	Index	123

1

EQUILIBRIA AND EQUILIBRIUM CONSTANTS

Introduction

One of the features which distinguishes science from other fields of human endeavour is its methods. In its simplest form, any scientific study begins with facts on which observers can agree. Facts give rise to hypotheses which suggest controlled experiments designed to yield further facts, and in turn to generate new hypotheses. From data established progressively in this cyclic way, generalizations are induced and subjected to further critical experimental test. The useful generalizations, the principles, the theories of science, are those which emerge temporarily triumphant from these never-ending attempts to disprove them. In seeking these generalizations, the aim is to be able to predict the behaviour of a particular system, be it a mechanism, a chemical reaction, or a physical transformation, which has not itself been studied experimentally. In this book we shall explore how some of these ideas work out in chemistry.

The ultimate aim in chemistry is to predict the chemical behaviour of all combinations of elements and compounds under all conditions. The combinations and the conditions which can be conceived to be of interest to mankind are beyond number, and we cannot hope to study them all experimentally. Chemistry deals with two related aspects:

(i) The properties of chemical substances.
(ii) The dynamics of chemical change.

and with the cognate question of how the behaviour of a substance in a chemical reaction may be predicted from a knowledge of its properties.

The Chemical Equation

A balanced chemical reaction states certain facts and asks a number of questions. For example, the equation

$$H_2\ (\text{gas}) + I_2\ (\text{gas}) \rightarrow 2HI\ (\text{gas}) \qquad (1)$$

states, among other things, that *if* hydrogen gas and iodine vapour were to react to give hydrogen iodide gas, they would do so in the molar ratio of 1 : 1. The information the equation does *not* give includes:

(i) Whether under specified conditions the reaction as written would proceed at all.
(ii) That if one mole of hydrogen gas and one mole of iodine vapour were mixed under specified conditions and reaction proceeds, whether, after the reaction has apparently ceased, the mixture would contain nothing but hydrogen iodide, or some hydrogen, some iodine, and some hydrogen iodide.
(iii) The rate at which hydrogen iodide, if any, is produced.
(iv) The mechanism by which the reaction, if any, proceeds.

Items (i) and (ii) may be combined in the single question, 'How *far* will the reaction as written proceed under specified conditions?' Items (iii) and (iv) pose the question, 'How *fast* will the reaction proceed under specified conditions?'

If we know the composition of the reaction mixture before any reaction takes place (i.e. the initial state) and the composition when no further reaction takes place no matter how long we wait (i.e. the final state) we shall have found an answer to the question, 'How far?', without any reference to the time t as a variable. In other words, our concern is only with the states at $t = 0$ and $t = \infty$, and with nothing which occurs between. On the other hand, if we seek an answer to the question, 'How fast?', we shall be vitally concerned not only with the composition of the reaction mixture at $t = 0$, but also with the composition at all values of t between $t = 0$ and $t = \infty$. In this case time is a variable.

The question of how far a chemical reaction may proceed is the concern of *chemical thermodynamics* and is time-independent. The question of how fast a chemical reaction proceeds is the subject of *chemical kinetics* and is time-dependent. It is vital to remember that these two questions are independent and distinct. We are in a fairly strong position to predict how far a given chemical reaction may proceed under specified conditions from the properties of the reactants and products, but, except in a comparatively few simple cases, we have only a rudimentary ability to make valid predictions of the rates of chemical reactions. Most of our discussion of the dynamics of chemical change will of necessity be concerned with the question, 'How far?', and only to a very limited extent in chapter 8 with the question, 'How fast?'

If any useful result is to be obtained in predicting how far a chemical reaction may proceed from a knowledge of the properties of the reactants and products, we have to answer the question, 'What properties will be relevant?' Will, for example, the properties of colour, density, solubility, melting point, boiling point, refractive index, specific heat, vapour pressure, be useful individually or collectively? How are these several properties, if they are the important ones, to be combined with appropriate weighting into some manageable quantity? Approaching the problem from this end does not seem likely to be very fruitful and we shall therefore first seek a way in which to state the answer to the question, 'How far?'

Reversibility and Equilibria

If ethyl alcohol and acetic acid are mixed in a particular molar ratio at a constant temperature of 25°C at 1 atmosphere pressure, and after a short period the reaction mixture is analysed, it will be found to contain ethyl alcohol, acetic acid, ethyl acetate, and water. The following equation may therefore be written:

$$\underset{\text{ethyl alcohol}}{C_2H_5OH} + \underset{\text{acetic acid}}{CH_3COOH} \rightarrow \underset{\text{ethyl acetate}}{CH_3COOC_2H_5} + \underset{\text{water}}{H_2O} \quad (2)$$

If ethyl alcohol and acetic acid are mixed in a particular molar proportion and the mixture maintained at constant temperature and pressure, samples withdrawn at intervals for analysis will after a time reveal that the mixture has reached a constant composition which does not change with further extensions of time. Moreover, if any two components on the same side of the equation, or any three or four of the substances are mixed in any proportion, it will be found that at constant temperature and pressure after a certain period of time all four components will be present in the mixture, and their concentrations will not vary further with time.

It is apparent that this reaction system has reached a state in which the variables of concentration, temperature and pressure do not appear to change with time. Such a state is said to be one of *equilibrium.* Two points are of special note:

(i) The equilibrium state may be approached from any direction.
(ii) The qualification, that the variables do not *appear* to change with time, emphasizes the dynamic rather than the static character of the equilibrium.

These points are illustrated in the following examples.

If 1 mole of ethyl alcohol and 1 mole of acetic acid are mixed at 25°C at 1 atm pressure and maintained under these conditions until equilibrium is established, analysis of the mixture will show that it contains:

ethyl alcohol	0·33 mole	in volume V
acetic acid	0·33 mole	in volume V
ethyl acetate	0·67 mole	in volume V
water	0·67 mole	in volume V

If 1 mole of ethyl acetate and 1 mole of water were mixed under the same conditions, the mixture at equilibrium would also contain the quantities set out above, and the same equilibrium position would have been achieved from both directions.

The fact that the concentrations of the four components are constant at equilibrium may be interpreted in two ways:

(i) That when a particular two-thirds of the molecules of ethyl alcohol react with a particular two-thirds of the molecules of acetic acid the whole process stops.
(ii) That the rates of the reactions of ethyl alcohol with acetic acid, and of ethyl acetate with water, are just balanced when the equilibrium composition is reached, but continue unabated in this nicely balanced way.

The first interpretation—a static one—implies the unacceptable proposition that there is something peculiar about two-thirds of the molecules of ethyl alcohol and acetic acid. The second interpretation—a dynamic one—requires no such improbable limitation. Equilibria in the kinds of systems with which we are concerned in chemistry are of this second dynamic kind.

If we had chosen a reaction of the same type represented by

$$A+B \rightleftharpoons C+D \tag{3}$$

in which, for initial amounts of A and B each of 1 mole, the concentrations at equilibrium were:

A	0·9999 mole	in volume V
B	0·9999 mole	in volume V
C	0·0001 mole	in volume V
D	0·0001 mole	in volume V

this is tantamount to saying that the reaction as written hardly proceeds at all, there being only very small concentrations of C and D at equilibrium. Alternatively, if the equilibrium concentrations were:

A	0·0001 mole	in volume V
B	0·0001 mole	in volume V
C	0·9999 mole	in volume V
D	0·9999 mole	in volume V

the reaction as written could be described as one which may proceed virtually to completion. The position of equilibrium thus affords a possible way of expressing the extent to which a reaction may proceed. Since the position of equilibrium can be approached from either direction, we may treat all chemical reactions as being formally reversible and indicate this by means of the double arrows. There will now be no formal distinction between reactants and products, but for convenience those appearing on the left of the equation are called *reactants* and those on the right *products*.

In the particular examples discussed so far equimolar initial concentrations have been used. What is required is a quantity which expresses the position of equilibrium not for any special set of initial conditions, but for all such sets of conditions. For a general reaction

$$a\mathrm{A}+b\mathrm{B} \rightleftharpoons c\mathrm{C}+d\mathrm{D} \tag{4}$$

an equilibrium constant K is defined by the equation

$$K=\frac{[\mathrm{C}]^c[\mathrm{D}]^d}{[\mathrm{A}]^a[\mathrm{B}]^b} \tag{5}$$

where [A] means the concentration* of A *at equilibrium* and [C], [B], and [D] have similar meanings with respect to substances C, B, and D respectively; *a*, *b*, *c*, and *d* are the numerical coefficients necessary to balance the equation, thereby ensuring that the Law of Conservation of Mass is obeyed. There is no reason in principle why the equilibrium constant should not have been defined by the inverse expression to (5), but, in order that everyone will use the same form, the convention of writing the concentration terms for the substances on the *right* of the chemical equation in the *numerator* has been widely adopted.

The Equilibrium Constant

For the example used in a previous section the equation may now be written

$$C_2H_5OH + CH_3COOH \rightleftharpoons CH_3COOC_2H_5 + H_2O \qquad (6)$$

and the equilibrium constant expressed by

$$K = \frac{[CH_3COOC_2H_5][H_2O]}{[C_2H_5OH][CH_3COOH]} \qquad (7)$$

At 25°C and 1 atm pressure for a mixture initially comprising 1 mole of acetic acid and 1 mole of ethyl alcohol in a volume V litres, the equilibrium concentrations of the four components have been found experimentally to be

$$C_2H_5OH \qquad \frac{0{\cdot}33}{V} \text{ mole l}^{-1}$$

$$CH_3COOH \qquad \frac{0{\cdot}33}{V} \text{ mole l}^{-1}$$

$$CH_3COOC_2H_5 \qquad \frac{0{\cdot}67}{V} \text{ mole l}^{-1}$$

$$H_2O \qquad \frac{0{\cdot}67}{V} \text{ mole l}^{-1}$$

The value of K at 25°C is therefore 4. From this one experiment we are now in a position to calculate the equilibrium concentrations at 25°C

* Strictly speaking, this should be the *activity* which, depending on the conditions, may differ from the concentration. For simplicity we shall consistently use the concentration in formulating equilibrium constants.

of the four components in any mixture made up initially from any two components appearing on the same side of the equation, or any three or four components in any proportions. For example, for a mixture of volume V litres comprising initially 2 moles ethyl alcohol, 3 moles acetic acid, and 1 mole of water, for which at equilibrium α moles of each have reacted or been formed, we have

Component	No. of moles initially	No. of moles at equilibrium	Concentration at equilibrium
C_2H_5OH	2	$2-\alpha$	$\frac{2-\alpha}{V}$
CH_3COOH	3	$3-\alpha$	$\frac{3-\alpha}{V}$
$CH_3COOC_2H_5$	0	α	$\frac{\alpha}{V}$
H_2O	1	$1+\alpha$	$\frac{1+\alpha}{V}$

and

$$K = \frac{\frac{\alpha}{V}\left(\frac{1+\alpha}{V}\right)}{\left(\frac{2-\alpha}{V}\right)\left(\frac{3-\alpha}{V}\right)} = 4 \tag{8}$$

This quadratic equation has two roots $\alpha = 5{\cdot}6$ or $1{\cdot}4$. The first may be rejected as being physically impossible, since it would result in negative values of the equilibrium concentrations of C_2H_5OH and CH_3COOH. The second enables the equilibrium concentrations of the four components listed above to be evaluated.

Since there are an infinite number of such mixtures, for each of which it is possible to calculate the equilibrium concentrations of the four components, we have reached the satisfying situation of being able to generate an infinite number of pieces of information from the value of K determined at this particular temperature and pressure essentially in a single experiment. This is a powerful illustration of prediction at work.

For an equilibrium system in which the components are all gaseous, it is convenient to express the equilibrium constant in a different form. In the reaction

$$N_2(g)+3H_2(g)\rightleftharpoons 2NH_3(g) \qquad (9)$$

as before
$$K_c=\frac{[NH_3]^2}{[N_2][H_2]^3} \qquad (10)$$

where the terms in the square brackets again represent the concentrations at equilibrium. To indicate this fact the subscript c has been added to K and henceforth this practice will be followed. If each of the gases is assumed to behave ideally and the concentrations are expressed in mole l^{-1}, the general gas law yields

$$p_{NH_3}=[NH_3]RT \qquad (11)$$

$$p_{N_2}=[N_2]RT \qquad (12)$$

$$p_{H_2}=[H_2]RT \qquad (13)$$

where the p's are the partial pressures of the respective components at equilibrium. Substitution in (10) gives

$$K_c=\frac{(p_{NH_3})^2}{(p_{N_2})(p_{H_2})^3}(RT)^2 \qquad (14)$$

A new constant K_p is defined by

$$K_p=\frac{(p_{NH_3})^2}{(p_{N_2})(p_{H_2})^3} \qquad (15)$$

which, in this example, is related to K_c by the equation

$$K_p=K_c(RT)^{-2} \qquad (16)$$

The power of the term RT has arisen from the fact that in (9)

$$\left(\begin{matrix}\text{No. of moles on the}\\ \text{right-hand side}\end{matrix}\right)-\left(\begin{matrix}\text{No. of moles on the}\\ \text{left-hand side}\end{matrix}\right)=-2 \qquad (17)$$

If we now write for the general case

$$\Delta n = \begin{pmatrix}\text{No. of gaseous moles} \\ \text{on the right-hand side}\end{pmatrix} - \begin{pmatrix}\text{No. of gaseous moles} \\ \text{on the left-hand side}\end{pmatrix} \quad (18)$$

then
$$K_p = K_c(RT)^{\Delta n} \quad (19)$$

In future K without a subscript will be used as a general expression for an equilibrium constant, and K_p and K_c employed for the specific cases in which the concentrations of the components at equilibrium are expressed as partial pressures and concentrations, respectively. Gases are, however, seldom ideal except at low pressures, and there are few liquid systems which exhibit ideal behaviour. The expressions for both K_p and K_c in terms of partial pressures and concentrations, respectively, are not, therefore, strictly accurate constants, but for many purposes may safely be treated as such.

For an equilibrium system in which some components are gases and some are condensed phases, e.g. solids or liquids, the equilibrium constant K_p takes a slightly different form. For example, in the reaction

$$NH_4HS(s) \rightleftharpoons NH_3(g) + H_2S(g) \quad (20)$$

the equilibrium constant K_p is written

$$K_p = (p_{NH_3})(p_{H_2S}) \quad (21)$$

The concentration (or partial pressure) of the condensed phase does not appear explicitly, because at moderate pressures the number of moles of NH_4HS per unit volume of solid ammonium hydrogen sulphide is constant, irrespective of whether the amount of solid present is 1 mg, 1 g, or 1 kg, and the equilibrium vapour pressure of $NH_4HS(p_{NH_4HS})$ will be constant at constant temperature. Similarly, the expressions for K_p for the corresponding reactions are as follows:

$$CaCO_3(s) \rightleftharpoons CaO(s) + CO_2(g) \qquad K_p = p_{CO_2} \quad (22)$$

$$C(s) + O_2(g) \rightleftharpoons CO_2(g) \qquad K_p = \frac{p_{CO_2}}{p_{O_2}} \quad (23)$$

$$2XO(s) + H_2(g) \rightleftharpoons X_2O(s) + H_2O(g) \qquad K_p = \frac{p_{H_2O}}{p_{H_2}} \quad (24)$$

For the reaction represented by (20) the equilibrium total pressure P at 25°C is found experimentally to be 50·6 cmHg. If NH_3 and H_2S behave as ideal gases, and since p_{NH_4HS} is small and may be neglected,

$$p_{NH_3} = p_{H_2S} = \frac{P}{2} \tag{25}$$

and K_p has a value at this temperature of 0·11 atm^2. The predictive gains here are rather different ones. From the value of K_p at 25°C, or directly from the fact that the equilibrium total gas pressure at this temperature is 50·6 cmHg, we may predict that it is impossible to decompose NH_4HS(s) totally at 25°C unless the evolved gas is removed in such a way as to maintain the pressure of gas in contact with the solid at less than the equilibrium value. Alternatively we may calculate the minimum amount of NH_4HS(s) which must be introduced into a vessel of given volume in order that the equilibrium condition may be achieved. What is of special interest in this example is how K_p varies with temperature. If we knew the value of the equilibrium constant at one temperature and its temperature coefficient, our predictive capacity would be greatly enhanced. In the next two chapters this is one of the important issues to be dealt with.

Problem 1.1

For the reaction

$$CH_3COOH + C_2H_5OH \rightleftharpoons CH_3COOC_2H_5 + H_2O$$

the equilibrium constant K_c at 25°C has a value of 4·0. Calculate the equilibrium concentrations in mole l^{-1} of the four substances in solutions prepared as follows:

(*a*) 3 moles CH_3COOH and 2 moles C_2H_5OH, the total final volume being 289 ml;
(*b*) 3 moles CH_3COOH, 2 moles C_2H_5OH, and 2 moles H_2O, the total final volume being 324 ml;
(*c*) 3 moles CH_3COOH, 2 moles $CH_3COOC_2H_5$, and 2 moles H_2O, the total final volume being 403 ml;
(*d*) 10 g $CH_3COOC_2H_5$ and 10 g H_2O, the total final volume being 21·2 ml;

If 100 ml of an inert solvent were added to each of the above mixtures,

(*e*) What would be the effect in each case on the equilibrium concentrations of the four substances?

Problem 1.2

Ethanol reacts with acetaldehyde according to the equation

$$2C_2H_5OH + CH_3CHO \rightleftharpoons CH_3CH(OC_2H_5)_2 + H_2O$$

At 25°C 1 mole of ethanol was mixed with 0·1 mole of acetaldehyde, and the reaction allowed to come to equilibrium. Analysis of the mixture, which had a final volume of 60 ml, showed that it then contained 0·01 mole of acetaldehyde.

(*a*) Write down the expression for the equilibrium constant K_c.
(*b*) Calculate the value of K_c and append its units.

Problem 1.3

For the reaction

$$SO_2(g) + \tfrac{1}{2}O_2(g) \rightleftharpoons SO_3(g)$$

at 500°C the equilibrium constant K_p is 85 when the partial pressures are expressed in atmospheres.

(*a*) Write down the expressions for K_p and K_c.
(*b*) Calculate K_p for the partial pressures expressed in mmHg.
(*c*) Calculate K_c at 500°C.

For the reaction

$$2SO_2(g) + O_2(g) \rightleftharpoons 2SO_3(g)$$

at the same temperature

(*d*) write down the expressions for K_p and K_c, and
(*e*) calculate K_p and K_c at this temperature.

Problem 1.4

For the reaction

$$PCl_5(g) \rightleftharpoons PCl_3(g) + Cl_2(g)$$

K_p at 623°*K* is 1·8, the partial pressures being expressed in atmospheres.

(*a*) Calculate the percentage conversion of PCl_5 to PCl_3 at equilibrium when the total pressure is 18 atm.
(*b*) Calculate the partial pressures of the three substances at equilibrium.

Problem 1.5

For the reaction

$$\tfrac{1}{2}SnO_2(s) + H_2(g) \rightleftharpoons \tfrac{1}{2}Sn(s) + H_2O(g)$$

the total pressure at equilibrium at 1023°K is $4{\cdot}20 \times 10^{-2}$ atm, the partial pressure of the water vapour being $3{\cdot}12 \times 10^{-2}$ atm.

(*a*) Calculate K_p for this reaction at this temperature. For the reaction

$$H_2(g) + CO_2(g) \rightleftharpoons CO(g) + H_2O(g)$$

K_p at 1023°K is 0·77.

(*b*) Calculate K_p at this temperature for the reaction

$$\tfrac{1}{2}SnO_2(s) + CO(g) \rightleftharpoons \tfrac{1}{2}Sn(s) + CO_2(g)$$

A stream of gas consisting of CO and CO_2 at a total pressure of 1 atm is passed over a sample of tin oxide at 1023°K.

(*c*) Calculate the composition of the gas stream which will just permit the reduction of tin oxide at this temperature.

Problem 1.6

The vapour pressure of water in equilibrium with a mixture of $CuCl_2.2H_2O(s)$ and $CuCl_2.H_2O(s)$ at 353°K is 0·32 atm and at 291°K it is 0·0049 atm.

(*a*) Write the reaction and express the equilibrium constant K_p.
(*b*) Calculate the values of K_p at these two temperatures.
(*c*) Will $CuCl_2.H_2O(s)$ be stable in contact with air at 291°K at a relative humidity of 76%? (Vapour pressure of water at 291°K = 15·5 mmHg.)

2

EQUILIBRIA AND ENERGY

Equilibria and Free Energy

The equilibrium constant as defined and illustrated in the preceding chapter gives a quantitative measure of the extent to which a chemical reaction may proceed. Our next aim is to see how such constants may be manipulated for the greatest gain from the least effort. Consider the two reactions

$$a\mathrm{A} \rightleftharpoons m\mathrm{M} + y\mathrm{Y} \qquad K_1 = \frac{[\mathrm{M}]^m[\mathrm{Y}]^y}{[\mathrm{A}]^a} \tag{1}$$

and

$$b\mathrm{B} + m\mathrm{M} \rightleftharpoons z\mathrm{Z} \qquad K_2 = \frac{[\mathrm{Z}]^z}{[\mathrm{B}]^b[\mathrm{M}]^m} \tag{2}$$

where the small letters are the numerical coefficients necessary to balance the equations. For a third reaction (3) which is the algebraic sum of (1) and (2)

$$a\mathrm{A} + b\mathrm{B} \rightleftharpoons y\mathrm{Y} + z\mathrm{Z} \qquad K_3 = \frac{[\mathrm{Z}]^z[\mathrm{Y}]^y}{[\mathrm{A}]^a[\mathrm{B}]^b} \tag{3}$$

it is obvious that

$$K_3 = K_1 K_2 \tag{4}$$

and, if K_1 and K_2 are known, K_3 can be found without experimental effort. While it is easy enough to deal with such simple combinations, more extensive or complex cases lead to cumbersome operations. Since addition of the reactions (1) and (2) is accompanied by multiplication of the corresponding equilibrium constants, the foreshadowed complexity would be greatly relieved if we could attribute to each reaction a quantity which was a logarithmic function of K. Such a quantity is given by the relationship

$$\Delta G^0 = -RT \ln K \qquad (5)^*$$

where ΔG^0 is called the *standard free energy change* for the reaction. For the moment, equation (5) may be looked on as a convenient arithmetical transformation and the standard free energy change simply as a name. For the example involving equations (1) to (4)

$$\Delta G_3^0 = \Delta G_1^0 + \Delta G_2^0 \qquad (6)$$

where ΔG_1^0, ΔG_2^0, ΔG_3^0 refer, respectively, to the equilibrium constants K_1, K_2, and K_3.

ΔG^0 for a reaction may be treated as part of the formulated reaction and an extensive property of it, i.e. it depends on the amounts of the various substances represented in the reaction. For example, for the reaction

$$H_2(g) + \tfrac{1}{2}O_2(g) \rightleftharpoons H_2O(g) \qquad (7)$$

ΔG^0 at 1000°K is $-45{\cdot}8$ kcal; if (7) were written

$$H_2O(g) \rightleftharpoons H_2(g) + \tfrac{1}{2}O_2(g) \qquad (8)$$

$\Delta G^0_{1000°K}$ would be $+45{\cdot}8$ kcal. Moreover, if (7) were multiplied throughout by 2 and written

$$2H_2(g) + O_2(g) \rightleftharpoons 2H_2O(g) \qquad (9)$$

$\Delta G^0_{1000°K}$ for equation (9) would be $-91{\cdot}6$ kcal. These properties of ΔG^0 are a necessary consequence of equation (5).

The following example further illustrates the algebraic manipulations of ΔG^0. Let us suppose that at 1000°K the values of ΔG^0 for the following reactions have been measured and the noted values obtained:

$$2Cu_2O(s) \rightleftharpoons 4Cu(s) + O_2(g) \qquad \Delta G^0_{1000°K} = 45{\cdot}6 \text{ kcal} \qquad (10)$$

$$H_2(g) + \tfrac{1}{2}O_2(g) \rightleftharpoons H_2O(g) \qquad \Delta G^0_{1000°K} = -45{\cdot}8 \text{ kcal} \qquad (7)$$

* 'ln' is used for logarithms to base e; 'log' for logarithms to base 10.

If (10) is divided by 2 and the result added to (7), we have

$$Cu_2O(s)+H_2(g) \rightleftharpoons 2Cu(s)+H_2O(g) \tag{11}$$

for which

$$\Delta G^0_{1000°K} = \tfrac{1}{2}(45{\cdot}6)-45{\cdot}8 = -23{\cdot}0\,\text{kcal}$$

If ΔG^0 for reactions of the type (10) for n different metal oxides were known, together with equation (7), values for n equations of the type (11) could be obtained. From $n+1$ pieces of information a further n pieces may thereby be generated without recourse to experiment.

An even more powerful illustration of this aspect of prediction at work is afforded by the next example. Again let us suppose that we have measured the values of ΔG^0 at, say, 1000°K for the reactions

$$3Cu_2O \rightleftharpoons 6Cu+\tfrac{3}{2}O_2 \qquad \Delta G^0_{1000°K} = 68{\cdot}4\,\text{kcal} \tag{12}$$

$$Al_2O_3 \rightleftharpoons 2Al+\tfrac{3}{2}O_2 \qquad \Delta G^0_{1000°K} = 325{\cdot}1\,\text{kcal} \tag{13}$$

Subtraction of (13) from (12) yields

$$3Cu_2O+2Al \rightleftharpoons Al_2O_3+6Cu \qquad \Delta G^0_{1000°K} = -256{\cdot}7\,\text{kcal} \tag{14}$$

Now there are about 100 elements, most of which combine with oxygen, many in several oxidation states. If there are, say, 200 such combinations, a knowledge of the values of ΔG^0 for the 200 appropriate reactions of type (12) would yield by simple combination two at time values of ΔG^0 for a further 19,900 reactions of type (14). The rate of interest on the experimental investment of 200 units is therefore about 10^4 per cent.

From the relationship between the standard free energy change for a reaction and the equilibrium constant, equation (5), the corresponding values of ΔG^0 and K for three temperatures are given in table 2.1 (p. 16).

Clearly, large negative values of ΔG^0 correspond to large values of K, and large positive values of ΔG^0 to small values of K. A large value of K, e.g. 10^{10}, means that the reaction as written may proceed virtually to completion; while a small value of K, e.g. 10^{-10}, means that the reaction as written does not proceed to any appreciable extent. The general criterion that a reaction may proceed virtually to completion is that it be accompanied by a large negative value of ΔG^0. Conversely, a large positive value of ΔG^0 means that the reaction as written will not proceed to any appreciable extent.

TABLE 2.1: CORRESPONDING VALUES OF ΔG^0 AND $\log K$ FROM THE EQUATION $\Delta G^0 = -RT \ln K$

T=298°K		T=500°K		T=1000°K	
log K	ΔG^0 kcal	log K	ΔG^0 kcal	log K	ΔG^0 kcal
−10	+13·7	−10	+23·0	−10	+46·2
−5	+6·9	−5	+11·5	−5	+23·0
−2	+2·7	−2	+4·6	−2	+9·2
0	0	0	0	0	0
+2	−2·7	+2	−4.6	+2	−9·2
+5	−6·9	+5	−11·5	+5	−23·0
+10	−13·7	+10	−23·0	+10	−46·2

There are many balanced reactions which can be written down on paper, but which when tried under particular conditions do not proceed. The problem of deciding whether such a reaction may proceed, and if so to what extent, is one which confronts every chemist in the laboratory and on the industrial scale. If it can be established by calculation that under all possible practical conditions the particular reaction would involve a large positive ΔG^0, the reaction may be discarded forthwith, since we can say positively that it will not proceed to a useful extent. If, on the other hand, the reaction involves for a particular set of conditions a large negative ΔG^0, all we can say is that it *may* proceed virtually to completion under these conditions. For a value of ΔG^0 which is positive but less than, say, 10 kcal at 1000°K, attention needs to be directed to the particular form of the expression for the equilibrium constant, in order to determine the equilibrium concentration of the desired product in relation to those of the reactants. For example, suppose that for the reaction

$$A_2(g) + B_2(g) \rightleftharpoons 2AB(g) \tag{15}$$

$\Delta G^0_{1000°K}$ is $+9{\cdot}2$ kcal. From table 2.1, K_p is 10^{-2} and is given by

$$K_p = 10^{-2} = \frac{p_{AB}^{\ 2}}{(p_{A_2})(p_{B_2})} \qquad (16)$$

If in a continuous-flow reactor A_2 and B_2 were each maintained at partial pressure of 0·5 atm pressure, then

$$p_{AB} = (0{\cdot}25 \times 10^{-2})^{\frac{1}{2}} = 0{\cdot}05 \text{ atm} \qquad (17)$$

Such an equilibrium yield, though small, may be quite acceptable in a continuous process in which the unreacted gases A_2 and B_2 can be recycled.

There is, however, another important consideration. As is shown below, ΔG^0 in general varies with the temperature, and in some cases may do so quite rapidly. The temperature T is, in addition, an explicit term in equation (5), and its effect on the value of K for a particular value of ΔG^0 is illustrated in table 2.1. If, therefore, the standard free energy change is to be used as a criterion for the feasibility of a reaction, it is essential that the value for the particular temperature in question be employed.

To this point, the standard free energy change has been introduced as a convenient alternative way of expressing an equilibrium constant, as a way of simplifying the combination of two or more equations, and as a means of defining the extent to which a reaction may proceed. If full benefit is to be obtained from this device and our original aim sustained, the next problem is to relate the change in the standard free energy for a reaction to the properties of the reactants and products.

Problem 2.1

The equilibrium constant K_p for the reaction

$$n\text{-butane(g)} \rightleftharpoons \text{isobutane(g)}$$

at 298°K is 2·54. Calculate the standard free energy change for the reaction at this temperature.

Problem 2.2

At 910°K, ΔG^0 for the reaction

$$C_2H_6(g) \rightleftharpoons C_2H_4(g) + H_2(g)$$

is $+$ 5·4 kcal.

(*a*) Calculate K_p at this temperature.

(*b*) Calculate the percentage of hydrogen in the equilibrium mixture at a total pressure of 1 atm.

Problem 2.3

The standard free energy changes at 298°K accompanying the reactions noted below are as follows:

$$H_2(g) + \tfrac{1}{2}O_2(g) \rightleftharpoons H_2O(l) \qquad \Delta G^0 = -56{\cdot}7\,\text{kcal}$$
$$H_2(g) + \tfrac{1}{2}O_2(g) \rightleftharpoons H_2O(g) \qquad \Delta G^0 = -54{\cdot}6\,\text{kcal}$$
$$C(s) + \tfrac{1}{2}O_2(g) \rightleftharpoons CO(g) \qquad \Delta G^0 = -32{\cdot}8\,\text{kcal}$$
$$C(s) + O_2(g) \rightleftharpoons CO_2(g) \qquad \Delta G^0 = -94{\cdot}3\,\text{kcal}$$

Calculate ΔG^0 and K_p for the following reactions at 298°K.

(*a*) $CO_2(g) + H_2(g) \rightleftharpoons CO(g) + H_2O(g)$
(*b*) $2CO(g) + O_2(g) \rightleftharpoons 2CO_2(g)$
(*c*) $C(s) + H_2O(g) \rightleftharpoons CO(g) + H_2(g)$
(*d*) $C(s) + 2H_2O(g) \rightleftharpoons CO_2(g) + 2H_2(g)$
(*e*) $H_2O(l) \rightleftharpoons H_2O(g)$
(*f*) From (*e*) calculate the equilibrium vapour pressure of water at 298°K.

Total, Fixed, and Free Energy

For the general reaction

$$aA + bB \rightleftharpoons cC + dD \tag{18}$$

the standard free energy change ΔG^0 is given formally by the equation

$$\Delta G^0 = (cG_C^0 + dG_D^0) - (aG_A^0 + bG_B^0) \tag{19}$$

where G_A^0 means the standard free energy per mole of the substance A, and G_B^0, G_C^0, and G_D^0 have similar meanings with respect to B, C, and D. If we had some independent way of determining G_A^0, G_B^0, G_C^0, and G_D^0, ΔG^0 for (18) could be obtained by simple arithmetic. Furthermore, if G^0 were know for all substances at all temperatures, it would be possible to calculate arithmetically ΔG^0 for any reaction at any temperature. Our problem reduces then to a consideration of the standard free energy of a substance, what it means, how it is expressed, how it is measured, and how it varies with temperature.

We start with a homely analogy. A man who earns a total salary of, say, £15 per week has to meet certain fixed commitments, e.g. his income tax as a member of the community, and his dues as a member of his union. The remainder of his salary, his free income, may be used as he chooses. His total income comprises two components such that

$$\text{total income} = \text{free income} + \text{fixed or organizational income} \tag{20}$$

His fixed income is the component concerned with the organizational aspects of his life, i.e. those aspects associated with the society in which he lives. If now his total salary is increased to £17 per week, this increase may be reflected in his free income, his fixed income, or in both. For example, if he jumps into a new taxation classification, he may find that all his increase is taken up in his fixed income, or he may find his free income increased by, say, 30/- a week and his fixed income by 10/- a week. If he buys a pair of shoes, he will exchange part of his free income for the shoes. The important point here is that his capacity to buy goods, i.e. his capacity to exchange money for goods, is determined not by his total income, but by his free income.

Energy is often defined as the capacity to do work, in much the same way as money may be thought of as representing capacity to purchase goods and services. Money is the medium of exchange in commercial transactions; energy is the medium of exchange in chemical reactions. In terms of our analogy, every chemical substance may be looked on as possessing a certain total energy comprising two components—the free energy, and the fixed or organizational energy—such that

$$\text{total energy} = \text{free energy} + \text{organizational energy} \qquad (21)$$

The free energy, then, is the component of the total energy which determines the capacity of a given substance to enter into a chemical reaction, i.e. to participate in an exchange of energy. In the simplest reaction represented by

$$A \rightleftharpoons B \qquad (22)$$

in which substance A is transformed into substance B, the capacity for this reaction to proceed is determined by the difference in the free energies of A and B. If, however, the reaction is actually carried out in a calorimeter in which the energy change can be measured, what will be determined is the change in total energy. This will be evident if we note that when 1 mole of A is transformed into 1 mole of B, both the free energy and the organizational energy are necessarily changed, and the measured quantity will be the change in the sum of these two quantities, i.e. the change in total energy. In summary, the free energy change determines the capacity for the reaction to proceed; the total energy change is the measured energy change when the reaction actually proceeds.

There is nothing very unusual in the measure of the capacity or potential to perform a particular task being different from the measured result manifested when the task is actually carried out. For example, it could be argued that because during the past twenty years England has had at least four times the population of Australia, it has had the capacity always to defeat Australia at tennis. The results of the Davis Cup matches actually played in this period clearly measure something different from this capacity.

The organizational energy of a substance is not a simply definable quantity. In a gas, except at elevated pressures, the molecules move about chaotically and there is no discernable order, whereas in a crystalline solid the atoms or molecules are arranged in an ordered manner and are able to move only very slightly about mean positions. Clearly, the organizational energy of a gas will be markedly different from that of a crystalline solid at the same temperature. One of the factors that determines the organizational energy is this degree of order which, in principle, could be expressed equally validly in terms either of the degree of order, or the degree of disorder. At very low temperatures gases and liquids condense to solids, and as the temperature is decreased towards 0°K the atoms or molecules in a crystalline solid are able to move less and less about their mean positions; at 0°K the solid approaches a state of perfect order. The degree of disorder, increasing with increasing temperature, is conveniently measured from this zero and is called the *entropy*. The other factor that determines the organizational energy is the temperature itself. We now rewrite (21) as

$$H = G + TS \tag{23}$$

where H is the total energy, more usually called the *enthalpy* or the heat content, G is the free energy, and S is the entropy. H, G, and S all vary with the temperature, but according to different laws. H and S do not vary much with temperature over a limited range, but from (23) G will do so to a much greater extent unless S happens to be very small.

The three quantities H, G, and S are all extensive properties of a substance, i.e. they depend on the amount of the substance to which they refer. H and G are usually expressed in calories or kilocalories per mole (kcal $mole^{-1}$) and S as calories per degree per mole (cal deg^{-1} $mole^{-1}$). The temperature T, always expressed in °K, is an intensive property, that is it is independent of the amount of substance being considered. For the general reaction

$$aA + bB \rightleftharpoons cC + dD \tag{18}$$

we may now write, following our established practice,

$$\Delta H = (cH_C + dH_D) - (aH_A + bH_B) \tag{24}$$

$$\Delta G = (cG_C + dG_D) - (aG_A + bG_B) \tag{25}$$

$$\Delta S = (cS_C + dS_D) - (aS_A + bS_B) \tag{26}$$

and by substituting (23) in (24) and simplifying it follows that

$$\Delta H = \Delta G + T\Delta S \tag{27}$$

This equation is often written in the form

$$\Delta G = \Delta H - T\Delta S \tag{28}$$

and from it ΔG can be calculated provided ΔH and ΔS are known at the appropriate temperature T. If, in addition, the manner in which ΔH and ΔS varied with temperature were known, ΔG at any temperature could be calculated. Our next task, in the light of equations (24) and (26), is to examine how for a given substance H, S, and their respective temperature coefficients may be determined and expressed.

Heat Capacity, Enthalpy, and Heat of Formation

One of the earliest experiments performed by students in physics is the measurement of the specific heat of a solid or of a liquid, that is the measurement of the amount of heat required to raise the temperature of 1 g of the substance through 1 deg C. In chemistry we are more interested in the *heat capacity* of a substance, which is the specific heat per mole and is usually expressed in cal deg^{-1} $mole^{-1}$. While it is simplest to measure this quantity for liquids and solids, there is no prohibitive difficulty in making measurements with gases, though it is necessary to distinguish between the heat capacity measured at constant pressure C_p and that at constant volume C_v. Here we shall be concerned only with the former.

The heat capacity of a substance measured at, say, 25°C is not necessarily the same as that measured at another temperature. For temperatures above 25°C the variation in heat capacity of a substance with temperature can usually be expressed by an equation of the form

$$C_p = a + bT \tag{29}$$

where a and b are constants which have different values for different substances. It is frequently found, however, that except over fairly short ranges of temperature the graph of C_p against T departs somewhat from a straight line, and it is necessary to introduce in equation (29) a further term in T^2 or T^{-2} in order more adequately to express the experimental data. We shall use equation (29) in the interests of simplicity.

Let us suppose for a moment that the heat capacity of a substance is constant between the temperatures T_1 and T_2, T_2 being higher than T_1. If H_{T_1} is the enthalpy of 1 mole of the substance at temperature T_1 and H_{T_2} the enthalpy at temperature T_2, it follows from the definition of the heat capacity C_p that

$$H_{T_2} = H_{T_1} + C_p(T_2 - T_1) \tag{30}$$

Since, in general, C_p is not constant but varies with temperature according to equation (29), the second term in (30) must be replaced by an integral giving

$$H_{T_2} = H_{T_1} + \int_{T_1}^{T_2} C_p \, dT \tag{31}$$

that is

$$H_{T_2} = H_{T_1} + a(T_2 - T_1) + \frac{b}{2}(T_2^2 - T_1^2) \tag{32}$$

To evaluate H_{T_2} it is necessary to know a, b, and H_{T_1}. While a and b may be determined from equation (29), we have no way of measuring in absolute terms the enthalpy of a substance at a particular temperature. We have therefore to resort to the device of an arbitrary zero to overcome this problem.

Consider the formation of the compound M_aX_b from its elements M and X according to the equation

$$aM + bX \rightleftharpoons M_a X_b \tag{33}$$

The heat of formation of the compound M_aX_b at temperature T is defined by the equation

$$\Delta H_T = H_{M_aX_b} - (aH_M + bH_X) \tag{34}$$

Let us suppose for a moment that we do have an absolute zero of enthalpy and examine the situation at temperature T graphically in figure 2.1.

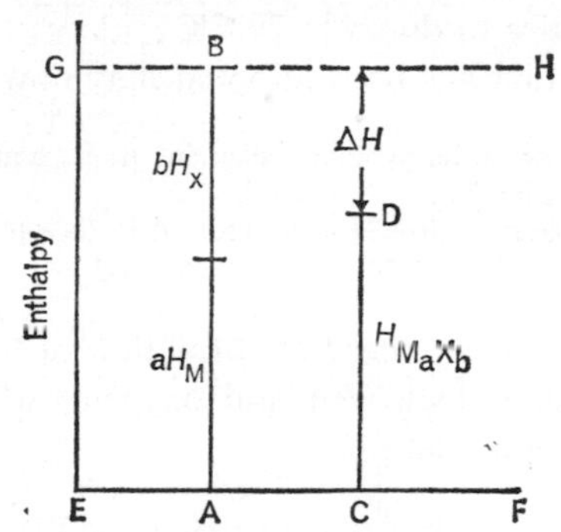

Fig. 2.1. Heat of formation of a compound from its elements

The ordinate AB measured from the absolute enthalpy zero represents the sum of the enthalpies of the reactants $(aH_M + bH_X)$ and the ordinate CD similarly represents the enthalpy of the product compound $(H_{M_aX_b})$ measured from the true enthalpy zero EF. The difference between GH and D is then ΔH and in this example will be negative, D being lower than GH. Now the value of ΔH will not change whether we use a true enthalpy zero, EF, or some arbitrary zero. If we choose as the arbitrary zero the line GH this is equivalent to making the enthalpy of a compound equal to the heat of the reaction in which the compound is formed from the elements. In so doing, we have effectively set the enthalpies of the elements at zero as the basis from which the enthalpies of compounds are measured.

Two other conditions need to be specified, namely, the *state* and the *temperature* to which the values refer. Normally the state chosen is the equilibrium state at the temperature in question, e.g. for oxygen it is gas at 1 atm pressure; for carbon it is a solid at 1 atm pressure, but which form of the solid? There are at least three possibilities, carbon (amorphous), graphite (crystalline), and diamond (crystalline). Since amorphous carbon may take many forms and may vary in properties, there are obvious advantages in choosing one of the crystalline forms. In practice graphite is chosen. Similar kinds of choices need to be made in some other cases, e.g. P, S, Sn. It might be thought appropriate to assign zero enthalpies to the elements at 0°K, but it is generally more convenient in practice to do so at 298°K.

The convention that has been adopted may now be summarized:

(i) The heat content or enthalpy of an element in its equilibrium state at 1 atm pressure at 298°K is zero.
(ii) The heat content or enthalpy of a compound in its equilibrium state at 298°K is equal to its heat of formation at this temperature.

For example, at 298°K the heat of formation of liquid water at 1 atm pressure from gaseous hydrogen and oxygen each at 1 atm pressure represented by the equation

$$\underset{(1\ \text{atm})}{H_2(g)} + \underset{(1\ \text{atm})}{\tfrac{1}{2}O_2(g)} \rightleftharpoons \underset{(1\ \text{atm})}{H_2O(l)} \tag{35}$$

is found by experiment to be $\Delta H_{298} = -68{\cdot}31$ kcal; the heat content or enthalpy of liquid water at 298°K is therefore $-68{\cdot}31$ kcal mole^{-1}.

To signify that this value refers to reaction (35), in which the reactants and product are in their *equilibrium* or *standard states*, we use the term *standard heat of formation*. Thus, in the above example, the standard heat of formation of liquid water at 298°K is written

$$\Delta H^0_{f298} = -68{\cdot}31 \text{ kcal mole}^{-1},$$

and for any element in its standard state we may write $\Delta H^0_{f298} = 0$.

There are reactions involving the formation of a single compound from its elements for which the heat of formation can be measured directly in a calorimeter. In other cases a combination of two or more measured reactions have to be used in order to obtain an equation of the type (35). Though direct calorimetric measurement is not the only way in which ΔH for a reaction may be determined, heats of formation of many compounds may be found by these direct methods. However,

TABLE 2.2: SAMPLE OF TABULATED STANDARD HEATS OF FORMATION AT 298°K

Substance	State	$\Delta H^0_{f\,298}$ kcal mole^{-1}	Substance	State	$\Delta H^0_{f\,298}$ kcal mole^{-1}
Al	s	0	CO	g	−26·4
Al_2O_3	s (α corundum)	−399·1	CO_2	g	−94·1
$AlCl_3$	s	−166·2	CH_4	g	−17·9
Ar	g	0	CH_3OH	g	−48·1
Br_2	l	0	CH_3OH	l	−57·0
Br_2	g	7·3	Cu	s	0
Br	g	26·7	Cu_2O	s	−39·8
Ca	s	0	CuO	s	−37·1
CaO	s	−151·9	H_2	g	0
$CaCO_3$	s (calcite)	−288·4	H_2O	g	−57·8
$CaCO_3$	s (aragonite)	−288·5	H_2O	l	−68·3
C	s (graphite)	0	HCl	g	−22·1
C	s (diamond)	0·5			

direct measurements of this kind cannot often be carried out with the elements and compounds in their respective standard states at 298°K, and it is frequently necessary to use some other conditions and to correct the results to these standard conditions for purposes of tabulation. In this or in other ways, it has been possible to tabulate standard heats of formation of the compounds at 298°K relative to the standard heats of formation of the elements at 298°K taken as zero. A sample of such a tabulation is given in table 2.2.

It may be noted that the state has to be carefully specified especially where there are two crystal forms, e.g. calcite and aragonite for $CaCO_3$. This extract includes the standard heats of formation of some common compounds, e.g. water and methanol, in both liquid and vapour states at 298°K. The usefulness of this will emerge in chapter 3.

If a full tabulation, of which table 2.2 is a minute sample, contained every element and compound, it would be possible to calculate arithmetically the standard enthalpy change for any reaction at 298°K. For example, for the reaction

$$Cu_2O(s)+H_2(g)\rightleftharpoons 2Cu(s)+H_2O(g) \quad (36)$$

$$\begin{aligned}\Delta H^0_{298} &= 2\Delta H^0_{f298}(Cu(s))+\Delta H^0_{f298}(H_2O(g)) - \Delta H^0_{f298}(Cu_2O(s))-\Delta H^0_{f298}(H_2(g))\\ &= 0 - 57{\cdot}8 - (-39{\cdot}8) - 0\\ &= -18{\cdot}0\,\text{kcal}\end{aligned} \quad (37)$$

The only limitation on this kind of calculation is the absence of the relevant numerical data. Strenuous efforts are continuously being made to improve the range, the accuracy, and the accessibility of such data. Some useful sources conveniently available are listed on p. 117.

Problem 2.4

From the data in table 2.2 calculate the standard enthalpy changes for the following reactions at 298°K.

(*a*) $Al_2O_3(s) + 3C\,(\text{graphite}) \rightleftharpoons 2Al(s) + 3CO(g)$
(*b*) $Al_2O_3(s) + 6HCl(g) \rightleftharpoons 2AlCl_3(s) + 3H_2O(g)$
(*c*) $2Al(s) + 3CaO(s) \rightleftharpoons Al_2O_3(s) + 3Ca(s)$
(*d*) $CaCO_3\,(\text{calcite}) \rightleftharpoons CaO(s) + CO_2(g)$
(*e*) $CH_4(g) + \frac{1}{2}O_2(g) \rightleftharpoons CH_3OH(l)$
(*f*) $H_2O(g) + Cl_2(g) \rightleftharpoons 2HCl(g) + \frac{1}{2}O_2(g)$
(*g*) $CH_3OH(g) + 3Cu_2O(s) \rightleftharpoons CO_2(g) + 2H_2O(l) + 6Cu(s)$

Entropy and Free Energy

In an earlier section of this chapter the total energy of a substance H was related to the free energy G and the organizational energy TS by the equation

$$H = G+TS \quad (23)$$

and in the last section the determination of H in terms of the heat of formation was outlined. Our next problem concerns the entropy S for, if it can be defined and determined, the free energy G may be calculated from (23). We have previously noted that the entropy is essentially a measure of atomic disorder, it being zero in the state of perfect order at 0°K and increasing with increasing temperature. From a practical viewpoint it is more convenient, however, to define the entropy of a substance in terms of the heat capacity which can be measured experimentally.

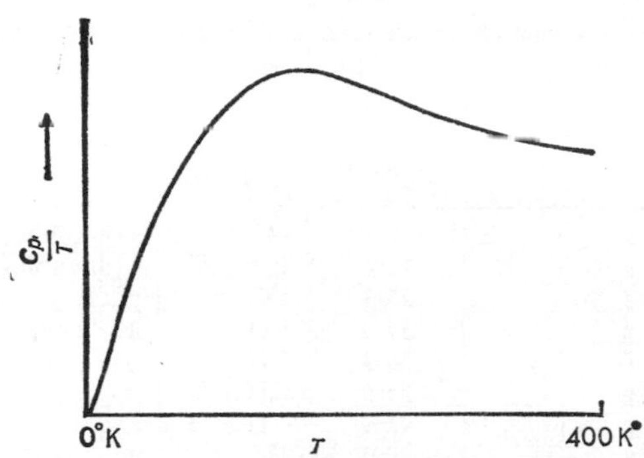

Fig. 2.2. The relationship between entropy and heat capacity

The heat capacity of a substance varies with temperature and if the quotient C_p/T, where T is in °K, is plotted against T, the type of curve obtained in the absence of physical transformations has the characteristics shown in figure 2.2.

The entropy of the substance at temperature T is defined by the equation

$$S_T = S_0 + \int_0^T \frac{C_p}{T} dT \tag{38}$$

where S_0 is the entropy at 0°K. Since entropy at 0°K for any ordered crystalline solid is zero, equation (38) reduces to

$$S_T = \int_0^T \frac{C_p}{T} dT \tag{39}$$

and the value of S_T is simply the area under the curve in figure 2.2 from 0°K to the temperature in question. If in the temperature range from 0 to T°K a physical transformation occurs, e.g. melting, it becomes necessary to obtain the entropy of phase I from 0°K to the transition point, the entropy change associated with the transition, and the entropy of phase II from the transition point to the temperature required. This complication will be considered in more detail at a later stage, but for the moment may be ignored.

TABLE 2.3: SAMPLE OF TABULATED STANDARD ENTROPIES AT 298°K

Substance	State	S^0_{298} cal deg^{-1} mole^{-1}	Substance	State	S^0_{298} cal deg^{-1} mole^{-1}
Al	s	6·8	C	s (graphite)	1·4
Al_2O_3	s	12·2	C	s (diamond)	0·6
$AlCl_3$	s	26·3	CO	g	47·3
Ar	g	37·0	CO_2	g	51·1
Br_2	l	36·4	CH_4	g	44·5
Br_2	g	55·6	CH_3OH	g	56·8
Br	g	41·8	CH_3OH	l	30·3
Ca	s	9·9	H_2	g	31·2
CaO	s	9·5	H_2O	g	45·1
$CaCO_3$	s (calcite)	22·2	H_2O	l	16·7
$CaCO_3$	s (aragonite)	21·2	HCl	g	44·6
Cu	s	8·0	O_2	g	49·0
Cu_2O	s	22·4	Cl_2	g	53·3

Unlike the values of enthalpies discussed in the last section which are related to an arbitrary zero, the entropies of substances defined by (39) can be determined absolutely and there are no impediments to recording the standard entropy values at 298°K. The symbol employed is S^0_{298} and from equation (39) it may be seen that the units will be the same as those for C_p, viz. cal deg^{-1} mole^{-1}. A small sample of these values is shown in table 2.3.

The direct measurement of heat capacity over a range from near 0°K to 298°K is not, however, the only means of determing S^0 at 298°K.

The values given in table 2.3 illustrate quantitatively how the entropy of a substance may be considered as a measure of the degree of disorder or randomness in a given state, an idea to which we have already referred. Gases are more disordered than liquids and liquids more disordered than crystalline solids, and for this reason the corresponding values of the standard entropy of a substance in the gaseous, liquid, and solid states decrease substantially in this order. For example at 298°K, $H_2O(g)$ has a value of 45·1 cal deg^{-1} mole^{-1}, $H_2O(l)$ one of 16·7 cal deg^{-1} mole^{-1}, while $H_2O(s)$ has a value of 11·5 cal deg^{-1} mole^{-1}. Another illustration is afforded by comparing the value of 55·6 cal deg^{-1} mole^{-1} for $Br_2(g)$ with 83·6 cal deg^{-1} mole^{-1} for the same weight of Br(g). The degree of disorder for the latter with twice the number of particles is necessarily much greater than for the same weight of diatomic bromine molecules. We may also note that the two crystalline forms of carbon and of calcium carbonate have slightly different values, indicating a different degree of disorder in these pairs of crystal structures at the particular temperature considered.

For gases of the same molecular configuration there is usually an increase in entropy with increasing molecular weight. For the diatomic gases, H_2, O_2, Cl_2, Br_2, the increasing molecular weights are reflected in the entropy values, namely 31·2, 49·0, 53·3, 55·6 cal deg^{-1} mole^{-1}. For solids and liquids the situation is more complicated because the degree of disorder (and hence the entropy) depends on the particular structure which the liquid or solid assumes. It is, however, generally true that the entropy of a gas per mole is greater than that of a liquid or solid. This generalization leads to a useful means of predicting by inspection the sign of the entropy change for a chemical reaction. We illustrate this by a few examples.

For the reaction

$$N_2(g)+3H_2(g) \rightleftharpoons 2NH_3(g) \tag{40}$$

$$\Delta S^0 = 2S^0(NH_3(g)) - S^0(N_2(g)) - 3S^0(H_2(g)) \tag{41}$$

and since the entropy of two moles of gas on the right-hand side of the equation, whatever the particular composition, will be less than that of the four moles on the left-hand side, ΔS^0 should be negative.

For the reaction

$$NH_4Cl(s) \rightleftharpoons NH_3(g)+HCl(g)$$

$$\Delta S^0 = S^0(NH_3(g))+S^0(HCl(g))-S^0(NH_4Cl(s))$$

and, since the sum of the molar entropies of the two gases on the right-hand side will be greater than the molar entropy of solid NH_4Cl, ΔS^0 for this reaction should be positive.

Similarly, for the reaction

$$C(s)+\tfrac{1}{2}O_2(g) \rightleftharpoons CO(g)$$
$$\Delta S^0 = S^0(CO(g)) - S^0(C(s)) - \tfrac{1}{2}S^0(O_2(g))$$

and with one gaseous mole on the right-hand side and half a gaseous mole on the left-hand side ΔS^0 should be positive. In contrast, for the reaction

$$C(s)+O_2(g) \rightleftharpoons CO_2(g)$$

with one gaseous mole on each side of the equation, all we can say is that ΔS^0 should be small, but we cannot without inserting the numerical values say what the sign is likely to be.

From the tabulated values for the standard heats of formation at 298°K, namely ΔH^0_{f298} (table 2.2), and standard entropies at 298°K, S^0_{298} (table 2.3), the standard free energy of formation of a compound at 298°K may be obtained in the manner illustrated below.

For the reaction

$$H_2(g)+\tfrac{1}{2}O_2(g) \rightleftharpoons H_2O(l) \qquad (35)$$

$$\begin{aligned}
\Delta H^0_{298} &= \Delta H^0_{f298}(H_2O(l)) - \Delta H^0_{f298}(H_2(g)) - \tfrac{1}{2}\Delta H^0_{f298}(O_2(g)) \\
&= -68{\cdot}3\,\text{kcal} \\
\Delta S^0_{298} &= S^0_{298}(H_2O(l)) - S^0_{298}(H_2(g)) - \tfrac{1}{2}S^0_{298}(O_2(g)) \\
&= \quad 16{\cdot}7 \quad - \quad 31{\cdot}2 \quad - \tfrac{1}{2}\times 49{\cdot}0 \\
&= -39{\cdot}0\,\text{cal deg}^{-1} \\
\Delta G^0_{298} &= \Delta H^0_{298} - T\Delta S^0_{298} \\
&= -68{,}300 + 298\times 39{\cdot}0 \\
&= -56{\cdot}7\,\text{kcal}
\end{aligned}$$

Hence the standard free energy of formation of $H_2O(l)$ at 298°K, ΔG^0_{f298}, is $-56{\cdot}7$ kcal mole^{-1}.

It follows that, given tabulations of ΔH^0_{f298} and S^0_{298} for elements and compounds, values of ΔG^0_{f298} could also be tabulated. Furthermore, for any reaction involving elements or compounds for which the values ΔH^0_{f298} and S^0_{298} are known, the values of ΔG^0_{298} may be calculated. For example, by using the data in tables 2.2 and 2.3 for the reaction

$$Cu_2O(s) + H_2(g) \rightleftharpoons 2Cu(s) + H_2O(g) \tag{36}$$

we have

$$\begin{aligned}
\Delta H^0_{298} &= 2\Delta H^0_{f298}(Cu(s)) + \Delta H^0_{f298}(H_2O(g)) \\
&\qquad\qquad - \Delta H^0_{f298}(Cu_2O(s)) - \Delta H^0_{f298}(H_2(g)) \\
&= \quad 0 \quad - \quad 57{\cdot}8 \\
&\qquad\qquad - \quad (-39{\cdot}8) \quad - \quad 0 \\
&= -18{\cdot}0\,\text{kcal} \\
\Delta S^0_{298} &= 2S^0_{298}(Cu(s)) + S^0_{298}(H_2O(g)) \\
&\qquad\qquad - S^0_{298}(Cu_2O(s)) - S^0_{298}(H_2(g)) \\
&= \quad 2 \times 8{\cdot}0 \quad + \quad 45{\cdot}1 \\
&\qquad\qquad - \quad 22{\cdot}4 \quad - \quad 31{\cdot}2 \\
&= 7{\cdot}5\,\text{cal deg}^{-1} \\
\Delta G^0_{298} &= \Delta H^0_{298} - T\Delta S^0_{298} \\
&= -18{,}000 - 298 \times 7{\cdot}5 \\
&= -20{,}240\,\text{cal}
\end{aligned}$$

and since

$$\Delta G^0 = -RT \ln K_p \tag{5}$$

$$\log K_{p298} = \frac{20{,}240}{1{\cdot}99 \times 298 \times 2{\cdot}303} = 14{\cdot}9$$

At this point it is worth pausing to see how far we have come. The example above shows how from a knowledge of two properties, the standard heat of formation and standard entropy of individual substances, we may predict the extent to which reactions involving these substances may proceed. One of the principal aims set out in chapter 1 has in this way been achieved, but at a single temperature of 298°K at which the thermal data have been recorded. Since we shall usually want to know the extent to which a reaction may proceed at temperatures other than 298°K, the next problem to be examined is how ΔG^0 and hence K vary with temperature.

Problem 2.5

From the data in table 2.3 calculate the standard entropy changes at 298°K for the seven reactions listed in problem 2.4.

Problem 2.6

By comparing the results obtained in problem 2.5 with the listed reactions, verify that, if the condensed phases are omitted from consideration, those reactions resulting in a substantial increase in the number of gaseous moles have large positive entropy changes and vice versa. Also confirm that where there is no change in the number of gaseous moles the entropy changes are small.

Problem 2.7

By combining the results obtained in problems 2.4 and 2.5, calculate the standard free energy changes at 298°K for the seven reactions listed.

Problem 2.8

From the data in tables 2.2 and 2.3, calculate the equilibrium vapour pressure of methanol at 298°K.

3

THE INFLUENCE OF TEMPERATURE ON EQUILIBRIA

The Nature of the Problem

We begin with the reaction

$$Cu_2O(s)+H_2(g) \rightleftharpoons 2Cu(s)+H_2O(g) \qquad (1)$$

for which we saw that

$$\Delta H^0_{298} = -18{\cdot}0\,\text{kcal}$$
$$\Delta S^0_{298} = 7{\cdot}5\,\text{cal deg}^{-1}$$
$$\Delta G^0_{298} = -20{\cdot}2\,\text{kcal}$$
$$\log K_{p298} = 14{\cdot}9$$

At 298°K the large value of K_p means that the reaction as written *may* proceed virtually to completion at this temperature. Under these conditions the reaction will be found to proceed extremely slowly, and in practice we are much more interested in what happens at higher temperatures—say 600°K. We therefore wish to know the value of ΔG^0_{600}.

At any temperature

$$\Delta G^0 = \Delta H^0 - T\Delta S^0 \qquad (2)$$

where ΔH^0 and ΔS^0 and hence ΔG^0 vary with temperature. A complete calculation must take full account of this variation. Such an approach is essential for reactions at very high temperatures common in metallurgical operations, whereas for the more modest conditions common in chemistry approximate treatments will frequently suffice. Two of these are outlined below.

A Very Approximate Treatment

Generally speaking, ΔH^0 and ΔS^0 do not themselves vary much with temperature over a few hundred degrees, and the principal change in ΔG^0 with temperature arises from the term $T\Delta S^0$ in equation (2). Under these conditions the following equation holds to a first approximation

$$\Delta G_T^0 \approx \Delta H_{298}^0 - T\Delta S_{298}^0 \tag{3}$$

At 600°K an approximate value of ΔG^0 for this reaction calculated from (3) would be −22·5 kcal. This is good enough for many purposes since errors introduced by the use of this approximation will not alter the conclusion that at 600°K the reaction as written may proceed virtually to completion. Furthermore, the accuracy with which the value of ΔH_{298}^0 is known is probably ± 1 kcal, and greater refinement is often not justified except at much higher temperatures.

Again from equation (3) the variation of ΔG^0 with temperature will be dominated by the sign and magnitude of ΔS^0. If ΔH^0 is negative and ΔS^0 is positive, ΔG^0 will become increasingly negative with increasing temperature. On the other hand, if ΔH^0 is negative and ΔS^0 is also negative, ΔG^0 will become less negative with increasing temperature. In the latter case, provided ΔS^0 and/or T is large enough, the $T\Delta S^0$ term will cause ΔG^0 to change from negative to positive as T is increased. For example, if for a reaction $\Delta H_{298}^0 = -20$ kcal, $\Delta S_{298}^0 = -50$ cal deg^{-1} and $\Delta G_{298}^0 = -5$ kcal, the approximate relationship (3) shows that ΔG^0 will change sign at about 400°K and will become increasingly positive at temperatures above this value.

It is emphasized that (3) is a rather crude approximation. For moderate temperatures it provides a rapid check on what happens to ΔG^0 with temperature and thereby greatly extends the immediate usefulness of the data of the type given in tables 2.2 and 2.3 and the simple calculations that are based upon them.

There is another instructive way of looking at this problem of the variation of K with temperature and of providing some experimental justification for this approximation. The following general relationships at any temperature T are already familiar:

$$\Delta G^0 = \Delta H^0 - T\Delta S^0 \tag{2}$$

and
$$\Delta G^0 = -RT \ln K \tag{4}$$

It follows that

$$\log K = -\frac{\Delta H^0}{2{\cdot}303RT} + \frac{\Delta S^0}{2{\cdot}303R} \tag{5}$$

Although ΔH^0 and ΔS^0 are themselves both functions of the temperature, the plot of directly measured experimental values of $\log K$ against $1/T$ over moderate temperature ranges (a few hundred degrees) is found to give for most reactions a straight line within the usual experimental errors. This means that over moderate temperature ranges both ΔH^0 and ΔS^0 do not vary very much and may be treated as being effectively constant.

Equation (5) also reveals that the sign of the slope of the $\log K$ versus $1/T$ plot will be determined by the sign of ΔH^0. If ΔH^0 is negative, the slope is positive, and as T is increased $\log K$ (and hence K) will decrease. If however ΔH^0 is positive, the slope is negative, and as T is increased $\log K$ will become less negative, i.e. K will increase. Whether $\log K$ at any particular temperature is positive or negative is not, however, determined by ΔH^0 alone, but by the relative values and signs of the two terms in (5), namely

$$\frac{-\Delta H^0}{2{\cdot}303RT} \quad \text{and} \quad \frac{\Delta S^0}{2{\cdot}303R}$$

Problem 3.1

Calculate the standard free energy changes at 900°K for the seven reactions listed in problem 2.4 making use of the approximation

$$\Delta G^0_T \approx \Delta H^0_{298} - T\Delta S^0_{298}$$

A More Exact Treatment

Over a moderate temperature range, say 100°K, the graph of $\log K$ against $1/T$ is, within experimental error, a straight line of slope $-\Delta H^0/2{\cdot}303R$, where ΔH^0 is the average standard enthalpy change for the reaction over the temperature range in question. More precise measurements show that the graph is not accurately linear, since ΔH^0 in general varies with temperature. In the limit it is necessary to express the variation of $\log K$ with temperature in terms of a differential equation

$$\frac{d\ln K}{dT} = \frac{\Delta H^0}{RT^2} \tag{6}$$

This equation, which is called the *van't Hoff equation*, expresses the fact that the slope of the $\log K$ versus $1/T$ graph at a particular temperature T_1 is given by $-\Delta H^0_{T_1}/2{\cdot}303R$, where $\Delta H^0_{T_1}$ is the particular value of ΔH^0 at the temperature T_1.

In chapter 2 we have seen that, in general, for any substance

$$H_T = H_0 + \int_0^T C_p\, dT \tag{7}$$

so that for any reaction we may write

$$\Delta H^0_T = \Delta H^0_0 + \int_0^T \Delta C^0_p\, dT \tag{8}$$

where ΔH^0_T is the standard enthalpy change for the reaction at temperature T, ΔH^0_0 is the standard enthalpy change for the reaction at 0°K and ΔC^0_p is the change in heat capacity for the reaction. It has also been noted that C^0_p varies with temperature, the simplest equation expressing this fact being

$$C^0_p = a + bT \tag{9}$$

It follows that

$$\Delta C^0_p = \Delta a + \Delta b\, T \tag{10}$$

An approximation of considerable utility ignores the temperature variation of ΔC^0_p and uses for this quantity over the temperature range in question its value at 298°K. Equation (8) then becomes

$$\Delta H^0_T = \Delta H^0_0 + \Delta C^0_{p298} \cdot T \tag{11}$$

and if the heat capacities of the elements and compounds at 298°K were tabulated, ΔC^0_{p298} could be conveniently calculated. In addition, if we know ΔH^0_T at 298°K, i.e. ΔH^0_{298}, for the reaction, ΔH^0_0 may be evaluated by substitution in (11).

Equation (6) may now be rewritten

$$\frac{d\ln K}{dT} = \frac{\Delta H_0^0 + \Delta C_{p298}^0 T}{RT^2} \tag{12}$$

which on integration gives

$$\log K = -\frac{\Delta H_0^0}{2{\cdot}303RT} + \frac{\Delta C_{p298}^0}{R}\log T + I \tag{13}$$

where I is an integration constant.

From ΔH_{298}^0 and ΔS_{298}^0, ΔG_{298}^0 and hence a value for $\log K_{298}$ may be obtained. Substitution in (13) of this value and that for ΔH_0^0 calculated from equation (11) permits I to be determined.

This procedure is illustrated for reaction (1), for which the necessary heat capacity data at 298°K are as follows:

Cu_2O(s) $\quad C_p^0 = 16{\cdot}7$ cal deg^{-1} mole^{-1}
H_2(g) $\quad C_p^0 = 6{\cdot}9$ cal deg^{-1} mole^{-1}
Cu(s) $\quad C_p^0 = 5{\cdot}8$ cal deg^{-1} mole^{-1}
H_2O(g) $\quad C_p^0 = 8{\cdot}0$ cal deg^{-1} mole^{-1}

$$\Delta C_p^0 = 2\times 5{\cdot}8 + 8{\cdot}0 - (16{\cdot}7 + 6{\cdot}9)$$
$$= -4{\cdot}0 \text{ cal deg}^{-1}$$

Since ΔH_{298}^0 for this reaction is $-18{\cdot}0$ kcal, substitution in (11) gives

$$-18{,}000 = \Delta H_0^0 - 4{\cdot}0 \times 298$$

whence $$\Delta H_0^0 = -16{,}810 \text{ cal}$$

Substitution in (13) gives

$$\log K = \frac{16{,}810}{2{\cdot}303RT} - \frac{4{\cdot}0}{R}\log T + I$$

and since $\log K_{298}$ is 14·9, I is obtained as 7·56. This equation now simplifies to the form

$$\log K = \frac{3670}{T} - 2{\cdot}01\log T + 7{\cdot}56 \tag{14}$$

from which K may be evaluated at any temperature T. For example, equation (14) gives the value of $\log K$ at 1000°K as 5·20. The very approximate treatment using equation (3) for this reaction gives a value of 5·60 at this temperature, whereas if no assumptions are made and an exact calculation not discussed here carried out in full, the value obtained is 5·12.

TABLE 3.1: EXTRACT OF TABULATED STANDARD HEAT CAPACITIES C_p^0 AT 298°K

Substance	State	C_p^0 cal deg^{-1} mole^{-1}	Substance	State	C_p^0 cal deg^{-1} mole^{-1}
Al	s	5·8	CO	g	7·0
Al_2O_3	s (α corundum)	18·9	CO_2	g	8·9
$AlCl_3$	s	21·3	CH_3OH	g	10·8
Ar	g	5·0	CH_3OH	l	19·2
Br_2	l	17·1	Cl_2	g	8·1
Br_2	g	8·6	Cu	s	5·8
Br	g	5·0	Cu_2O	s	16·7
Ca	s	6·3	CuO	s	10·6
CaO	s	10·2	H_2	g	6·9
$CaCO_3$	s (calcite)	19·6	H_2O	g	8·0
$CaCO_3$	s(aragonite)	19·4	H_2O	l	18·0
C	s (graphite)	2·1	HCl	g	7·0
C	s (diamond)	1·4	O_2	g	7·0
CH_4	g	9·5			

This is a typical situation in which for most temperatures of interest in chemistry there is little gain in taking into account the variation of ΔC_p^0 with temperature. Table 3.1 records a few examples of heat capacities at 298°K of which a large number have been measured and recorded in the literature. From these ΔC_{p298}^0 may be calculated for any given reaction.

Within the limits of availability of data on standard heats of formation (table 2.2), standard entropies (table 2.3), and standard heat capacities (table 3.1) we are now in a position to calculate the equilibrium constant for any reaction at any temperature. There are, however a few complications, the most important being the occurrence of changes of state in reactants and products, and the energy changes associated with them. This is the next problem to be tackled.

Problem 3.2

For the reaction

$$CuCl_2.2H_2O(s) \rightleftharpoons CuCl_2.H_2O(s) + H_2O(g)$$

the values of the equilibrium constant at several temperatures are as follows:

T°K	291	313	333	353
K_p atm	0·0049	0·0247	0·100	0·322

(*a*) Determine the average standard enthalpy change over the range 291–353°K.
(*b*) Calculate the standard free energy change at 353°K.
(*c*) Calculate the standard entropy change at 353°K.

Problem 3.3

For the reaction

$$C_2H_4(g) + H_2O(g) \rightleftharpoons C_2H_5OH(g)$$

the values of K_p at several temperatures are as follows:

T°K	418	448	473	498	523
K_p atm^{-1}	$6{\cdot}8\times10^{-2}$	$3{\cdot}6\times10^{-2}$	$1{\cdot}65\times10^{-2}$	$1{\cdot}07\times10^{-2}$	$6{\cdot}7\times10^{-3}$

(*a*) Determine the average standard enthalpy change over the range 418–523°K.
(*b*) Calculate the standard free energy change at 460°K.
(*c*) Calculate the standard entropy change at 460°K.

Problem 3.4

Calculate the standard free energy changes at 900°K for the seven reactions listed in problem 2.4, and compare the results with those obtained in problem 3.1. The heat capacity data required are listed in table 3.1.

Changes of State—Physical Equilibria

In tables 2.2, 2.3, and 3.1 care has been taken to specify the physical state to which the recorded data at 298°K refer. For the reaction

$$H_2(g) + \tfrac{1}{2}O_2(g) \rightleftharpoons H_2O(l) \qquad (15)$$

at 298°K, ΔH^0 is simply the standard heat of formation of liquid water at this temperature, namely $-68{\cdot}3$ kcal, and as we have values for the entropies and heat capacities of $H_2(g)$, $O_2(g)$, and $H_2O(l)$ from tables 2.3 and 3.1, we can calculate ΔG^0 for this reaction at any temperature.

At 1000°K for example, the water is obviously in the vapour state and we are more likely to be interested in finding ΔG^0_{1000} not for reaction (15), but for

$$H_2(g)+\tfrac{1}{2}O_2(g)\rightleftharpoons H_2O(g) \tag{16}$$

The transformation of $H_2O(l)$ to $H_2O(g)$ at 1 atm pressure will take place at the normal boiling point of water, namely 373°K. Before outlining the steps necessary to obtain ΔG^0_{1000} for (16), consider first the reaction

$$H_2O(l)\rightleftharpoons H_2O(g) \tag{17}$$

for which at 373°K ΔH^0_{373} will be the latent heat of vaporization per mole at this temperature. The standard free energy change at 373°K, namely ΔG^0_{373}, will be zero as the following argument shows:

For (17) $H_2O(l)$ is a condensed phase and the equilibrium constant is therefore expressed as

$$K_p = p_{H_2O} \tag{18}$$

At 373°K, $p_{H_2O} = 1$ atm and hence $K_p = 1$ and ΔG^0_{373} which is given by

$$\Delta G^0 = -RT\ln K_p \tag{4}$$

will be zero. It follows that for (17)

$$\frac{\Delta H^0_{373}}{373} = \Delta S^0_{373} \tag{19}$$

so that provided we know the latent heat of vaporization at the boiling-point, the enthalpy and entropy changes for (17) at this temperature are defined.

To obtain ΔG^0_{1000} for (16) we may now proceed by the following steps:

(i) Determine ΔH^0_{373}, ΔS^0_{373} and ΔG^0_{373} for (15).

(ii) Note that for (17) ΔG^0_{373} is zero and ΔS^0_{373} is $\Delta H^0_{373}/373$, where ΔH^0_{373} is the latent heat of vaporization per mole at 373°K.

(iii) Add equations (15) and (17) to yield (16) for which ΔH^0_{373}, ΔS^0_{373}, and ΔG^0_{373} may be obtained by the addition of the corresponding values for (15) and (17).

We now have the values for ΔH^0, ΔS^0, and ΔG^0 for the required reaction at one particular temperature. The only difference is that the temperature is 373°K and not 298°K, and the procedure for determining ΔG^0 and hence K_p at some other higher temperature follows exactly the pattern outlined in the previous section.

Though this is a simple example and the procedure a standard one applicable to other cases of changes of state, e.g. melting, transition from one solid phase to another, there would be considerable practical gain if, in addition to tabulating the standard heat of formation and entropy of $H_2O(l)$ at 298°K, the corresponding values for $H_2O(g)$, calculated back to 298°K were also recorded. It would then be possible to write down directly the values of ΔH^0, ΔS^0, ΔG^0, and ΔC_p^0 at 298°K for the reaction (16) and to calculate in a direct manner $\log K_p$ at any desired temperature without having to take into account the phase change at 373°K. Similarly, there would be equally great advantages in tabulating the standard values at 298°K for the several phases of a substance of interest, even though all but one will not be the stable form at 1 atm pressure at this temperature. Accordingly, values of ΔH_f^0, S^0, and C_p^0 for $H_2O(g)$ at 298°K are included in tables 2.2, 2.3, and 3.1, respectively. Values for the two crystalline forms of carbon and of $CaCO_3$ are also tabulated for the same reasons.

In estimating these values at 298°K for $H_2O(g)$ we make use of the standard procedures and equations with which we are already familiar. Since we have values for ΔH^0, ΔS^0, and ΔG^0 for reaction (16) at 373°K we need to be able to calculate the values of at least two of these quantities for this reaction at 298°K. Either of the methods given in the two preceding sections may be used, the only difference being that we now wish to calculate the data for a lower temperature (298°K) from known data at a higher value of 373°K. Previously the task was to calculate the data for a higher temperature from known data at a lower temperature, usually 298°K.

One further useful relationship arises from the treatment of the vaporization of water as a chemical reaction. For equation (17) we wrote

$$K_p = p_{H_2O} \tag{18}$$

where p_{H_2O} is the equilibrium vapour pressure at the temperature in question. The van't Hoff equation,

$$\frac{d \ln K}{dT} = \frac{\Delta H^0}{RT^2} \qquad (6)$$

now becomes

$$\frac{d \ln p_{H_2O}}{dT} = \frac{\Delta H^0}{RT^2} \qquad (20)$$

where ΔH^0 is now the enthalpy change for the reaction (17), i.e. the latent heat of vaporization per mole. This equation, known as the *Clausius-Clapeyron equation*, may be integrated in the same way as for the van't Hoff equation to express the variation of vapour pressure of a liquid with temperature. This discussion is not restricted to liquid/gas systems, but may be extended to other cases of physical equilibria between phases of the same substance. What we have done, in effect, is to treat these physical transformations formally as chemical reactions, of which they are but a special case, and to apply to them the principles that have been outlined for handling chemical equilibria.

Problem 3.5

For the reaction

$$C_2H_5OH(l) + 3O_2(g) \rightleftharpoons 2CO_2(g) + 3H_2O(l)$$

$\Delta H^0_{298} = -327{\cdot}6$ kcal and $\Delta S^0_{298} = -33{\cdot}1$ cal deg^{-1}. Calculate the equilibrium constant K_p at 600°K for the reaction

$$C_2H_5OH(g) + 3O_2(g) \rightleftharpoons 2CO_2(g) + 3H_2O(g)$$

The following data in addition to those given in the tables in chapters 2 and 3 are required:

$$\text{b.p. } C_2H_5OH = 351{\cdot}5\text{°K}$$

latent heat of vaporization of C_2H_5OH at b.p. $= 9{\cdot}2$ kcal mole^{-1}

$$C^0_p\ (C_2H_5OH(g)) = 20{\cdot}9 \text{ cal deg}^{-1}\text{mole}^{-1}$$

The Laws of Thermodynamics

These first three chapters provide many of the working tools required in the remaining five. At various points relationships have been introduced without formal proof and have been explained or justified in terms of experimental observations or by analogies akin to common experience. The principles that have been used rest on the three Laws of Thermodynamics.

The first of these is the Law of Conservation of Energy which we have used implicitly by associating with a chemical reaction a particular energy, entropy, or heat capacity change and of performing on that quantity the same algebraic manipulations as we have carried out with the reaction itself. For example, when we have added two reactions together to get a third, we have also added the two corresponding energy terms to obtain the quantity corresponding to the third reaction. This and similar manipulations are justified either in terms of the general statement of the First Law that energy cannot be created or destroyed, or of a particular form called *Hess's law of constant heat summation.* This states that the resultant heat change for a chemical reaction is the same whether it is carried out in one stage or in several.

The Third Law is also capable of simple definition. In figure 2.2 the graph of C_p/T against T has been extrapolated through the origin at 0°K and the entropy of a crystalline solid at 0°K was equated to zero. This is, for our purposes, an adequate definition of the Third Law of Thermodynamics.

The Second Law may be stated in many different ways, depending on whether one is conversing with an engineer, a physicist, or a chemist, or discussing a steam engine, a physical change, or a chemical reaction. No definition in isolation from a full discussion of the background which gave it birth is significant, and for our present purposes it is important first to note some of the principal consequences of the Second Law of practical utility to the chemist. Among others, the key equations of which we have made extensive use

$$G = H - TS$$

$$\Delta G^0 = -RT \ln K$$

$$\frac{d \ln K}{dT} = \frac{\Delta H^0}{RT^2}$$

are all manifestations of the Second Law.

In its most general form the Second Law may be stated as follows:

'Every system which is left to itself will, on the average, change towards a condition of maximum probability.'

The essential feature of this law and its application to energy changes in chemistry emerges if we rewrite it in a slightly modified and somewhat less general way as:

'Every system which is left to itself will change in such a way as to approach a definite state of equilibrium.'

Some familiar examples of this law at work include:

(i) The spontaneous diffusion of a solute from a concentrated solution into a dilute leading towards a condition of uniform concentration.
(ii) The spontaneous passage of heat from a hot to a cold body leading to a condition of uniform temperature.
(iii) The spontaneous oxidation of organic compounds by the atmosphere.
(iv) The spontaneous passage of a chemical reaction from an initial state to a definite state of equilibrium.

4

ENERGY CHANGES IN SOLUTIONS

Enthalpies of Solution

Almost everyone who has worked in a chemical laboratory has noticed that when concentrated sulphuric acid is diluted with water, or solid sodium hydroxide is dissolved in water, heat is evolved. These are examples of a general phenomenon—that when a solute is dissolved in a solvent heat may be evolved or absorbed. The enthalpy change observed depends, amongst other things, on the concentration of the final solution. The solution process of, say, 1 mole of HCl(g) in 5 moles of water may be represented by the equation

$$HCl(g) + 5H_2O(l) \rightleftharpoons HCl \text{ in } 5H_2O(l) \qquad \Delta H = -15{\cdot}3\,\text{kcal} \qquad (1)$$

for which the enthalpy change per mole of solute, namely $-15{\cdot}3$ kcal, is called the *integral heat of solution.* In 15 moles of water ΔH is $-17{\cdot}0$ kcal; in 200 moles of water it is $-17{\cdot}7$ kcal; and in 10,000 moles $-17{\cdot}9$ kcal.

The experimental values of the integral heats of solution of a solute approach a limiting value as the concentration decreases. For HCl(g), for example, this value is $-17{\cdot}96$ kcal and the corresponding process may be represented by the equation

$$HCl(g) + aq \rightleftharpoons HCl(aq) \qquad \Delta H = -17{\cdot}96\,\text{kcal} \qquad (2)$$

where 'aq' is intended to represent an amount of water so large that any further dilution produces no perceptible heat change. The integral heats of solution in water at 298°K of a few solutes in 200 moles of water are listed in table 4.1.

The variety of both positive and negative values of ΔH in table 4.1 suggests that solution involves more than one elementary process and that the measured heat is the resultant of several processes. In the solution of sodium chloride in water we might have expected that ΔH would be large and positive due to the absorption of the energy required to overcome the strong interionic attraction between sodium ions and chloride ions in the crystal lattice. There is, however, at least one other process, namely the combination of the ions with the solvent, which we call *solvation* and which is exothermic. For sodium chloride these two energy changes of opposite sign nearly balance, giving a small resultant positive value of the integral heat of solution for this salt.

TABLE 4.1: INTEGRAL HEATS OF SOLUTION IN 200 MOLES OF WATER AT 298°K

Solute	ΔH kcal mole^{-1}	Solute	ΔH kcal mole^{-1}
HCl(g)	−17·74	NaOH(s)	−10·11
HBr(g)	−20·05	KOH(s)	−13·04
HI(g)	−7·02	NH_3(g)	−8·28
H_2SO_4(l)	−17·91	NaCl(s)	1·02
HNO_3(l)	−7·84	KCl(s)	4·20
CH_3COOH(l)	−0·32	NH_4NO_3(s)	6·08

Equations of the type (1) and (2) may be added or subtracted to obtain the enthalpy change for other processes. For example,

$$\mathrm{HCl(g)+5H_2O(l)\rightleftharpoons HCl\ in\ 5H_2O(l)} \qquad \Delta H = -15{\cdot}3\,\mathrm{kcal} \quad (1)$$

$$\mathrm{HCl(g)+200H_2O(l)\rightleftharpoons HCl\ in\ 200H_2O(l)} \qquad \Delta H = -17{\cdot}7\,\mathrm{kcal} \quad (3)$$

Subtraction of (1) from (3) yields

$$\mathrm{HCl\ in\ 5H_2O(l)+195H_2O(l)\rightleftharpoons HCl\ in\ 200H_2O(l)} \quad \Delta H = -2{\cdot}4\,\mathrm{kcal} \quad (4)$$

where $-2{\cdot}4$ kcal is called the *integral heat of dilution* of HCl(g) between the two concentrations noted.

Integral heats of solution may also be used to determine the enthalpy change accompanying formation of solid hydrates from the corresponding anhydrous salts. For example, the enthalpy changes for reactions (5) and (6) can be conveniently measured.

$$Na_2SO_4(s)+aq \rightleftharpoons Na_2SO_4(aq) \qquad \Delta H = -0{\cdot}6\,\text{kcal} \qquad (5)$$

$$Na_2SO_4\,.\,10H_2O(s)+aq \rightleftharpoons Na_2SO_4(aq) \qquad \Delta H = +18{\cdot}8\,\text{kcal} \qquad (6)$$

Subtraction of (6) from (5) yields

$$Na_2SO_4(s)+10H_2O(l) \rightleftharpoons Na_2SO_4\,.\,10H_2O(s) \qquad \Delta H = -19{\cdot}4\,\text{kcal} \qquad (7)$$

The subtraction here is valid since 'aq' represents so large an amount of water that 10 H_2O may be taken from it without any significant heat effect.

It is sometimes convenient when considering enthalpy changes of reactions in aqueous solution to have available for direct use enthalpies of formation of various solutes. For example, the standard enthalpy of formation of HCl(g) at 298°K is $-22{\cdot}1$ kcal and the standard integral heat of solution of HCl in 200 moles of H_2O is $-17{\cdot}7$ kcal, that is

$$\tfrac{1}{2}H_2(g)+\tfrac{1}{2}Cl_2(g) \rightleftharpoons HCl(g) \qquad \Delta H^0_{298} = -22{\cdot}1\,\text{kcal} \qquad (8)$$

and

$$HCl(g)+200H_2O(l) \rightleftharpoons HCl \text{ in } 200H_2O(l) \qquad \Delta H^0_{298} = -17{\cdot}7\,\text{kcal} \qquad (9)$$

whence by addition

$$\tfrac{1}{2}H_2(g)+\tfrac{1}{2}Cl_2(g) +200H_2O(l) \rightleftharpoons HCl \text{ in } 200H_2O(l) \qquad \Delta H^0_{298} = -39{\cdot}8\,\text{kcal} \qquad (10)$$

In a like manner the values listed in table 4.2 have been obtained.

From the data in table 4.2 the standard enthalpy of neutralization of an acid and base may be calculated. We may write

$$NaOH \text{ in } 100H_2O(l)+HCl \text{ in } 100H_2O(l) \rightleftharpoons NaCl \text{ in } 200H_2O(l)+H_2O(l) \qquad (11)$$

TABLE 4.2: STANDARD ENTHALPIES OF FORMATION OF SOLUTES IN AQUEOUS SOLUTION

Solute	In 100 H_2O kcal mole^{-1}	In 200 H_2O kcal mole^{-1}	In ∞ H_2O kcal mole^{-1}
$NaOH$	−112·1	−112·1	−112·2
$NaCl$	−97·2	−97·2	−97·3
HCl	−39·7	−39·8	−40·0
HNO_3	−49·2	−49·2	−49·4
CH_3COOH	−116·7	−116·7	−116·7
CH_3COONa	−173·8	−173·9	−174·1

and from the data in table 4.2 and the standard heat of formation of $H_2O(l)$ at 298°K of −68·3 kcal mole^{-1}

$$\Delta H^0_{298} = -97{\cdot}2-68{\cdot}3+39{\cdot}7+112{\cdot}1$$
$$= -13{\cdot}7 \text{ kcal}$$

Similar calculations for the systems

$$NaOH—HNO_3, \quad NaOH—CH_3COOH$$

yield values of ΔH^0_{298} of −13·7 and −13·4 kcal, respectively. If the reaction of NaOH is extended to a variety of other acids under similar conditions, it is found that some yield a common value for the enthalpy of neutralization of −13·7 kcal, while others, of which acetic acid is an example, give values which are numerically less than this figure. We might on this basis classify acids into two groups: strong acids which yield the value of −13·7 kcal, and weak acids which give smaller numerical values. If we accept that NaOH is fully dissociated according to the equation

$$NaOH(aq) \rightleftharpoons Na^+(aq) + OH^-(aq) \tag{12}$$

and that strong acids and salts are also fully dissociated,

$$HA(aq) \rightleftharpoons H^+(aq) + A^-(aq) \tag{13}$$

it follows that the limiting value of −13·7 kcal results wholly from the reaction

$$H^+(aq) + OH^-(aq) \rightleftharpoons H_2O(l) \tag{14}$$

The lower numerical value of ΔH, corresponding to a smaller evolution of heat for the neutralization of NaOH with weak acids, may be interpreted in the absence of interfering factors as arising from the absorption of energy in the dissociation of the otherwise not fully dissociated weak acid. A similar interpretation may be used in dealing with the heat of neutralization of a strong acid with weak bases. In both cases the numerical decrease from $-13{\cdot}7$ kcal could be taken as a criterion for arranging acids and bases in order of their strengths. This is not, however, recommended since there are some cases in which the decrease is due to other causes.

Enthalpies of Formation of Ions

For strong electrolytes in dilute solution we have seen that

$$H^+(aq)+OH^-(aq) \rightleftharpoons H_2O(l) \qquad \Delta H^0_{298} = -13{\cdot}7\,\text{kcal} \qquad (14)$$

and from the standard enthalpy of formation of $H_2O(l)$

$$H_2(g)+\tfrac{1}{2}O_2(g) \rightleftharpoons H_2O(l) \qquad \Delta H^0_{298} = -68{\cdot}3\,\text{kcal} \qquad (15)$$

By subtracting (14) from (15) it follows that

$$H_2(g)+\tfrac{1}{2}O_2(g) \rightleftharpoons H^+(aq)+OH^-(aq) \qquad \Delta H^0_{298} = -54{\cdot}6\,\text{kcal} \qquad (16)$$

The enthalpies of formation of the individual ions H^+ (aq) and OH^- (aq) cannot be separately determined, but if we adopt an arbitrary scale defined by

$$\tfrac{1}{2}H_2(g)+aq \rightleftharpoons H^+(aq)+e \qquad \Delta H^0_{298} = 0 \qquad (17)$$

the standard enthalpies of formation of other ions in aqueous solutions may be tabulated relative to the standard enthalpy of formation of H^+ (aq) taken as zero. By combining (16) and (17), and recalling the meaning of 'aq' in these equations

$$\tfrac{1}{2}H_2(g)+\tfrac{1}{2}O_2(g)+aq+e \rightleftharpoons OH^-(aq) \qquad \Delta H^0_{298} = -54{\cdot}6\,\text{kcal} \qquad (18)$$

and by combining (17) with the equation

$$\tfrac{1}{2}H_2(g)+\tfrac{1}{2}Cl_2(g)+aq \rightleftharpoons H^+(aq)+Cl^-(aq) \quad \Delta H^0_{298} = -40{\cdot}0\,\text{kcal} \qquad (19)$$

we have

$$\tfrac{1}{2}Cl_2(g) + aq + e \rightleftharpoons Cl^-(aq) \qquad \Delta H^0_{298} = -40{\cdot}0\,\text{kcal} \qquad (20)$$

If this procedure is continued, it is possible to prepare a table of the standard enthalpies of formation of ions in aqueous solution. Some examples are given in table 4.3.

TABLE 4.3: STANDARD ENTHALPIES OF FORMATION OF IONS IN AQUEOUS SOLUTION AT 298°K

Ion	Enthalpy kcal mole^{-1}	Ion	Enthalpy kcal mole^{-1}	Ion	Enthalpy kcal mole^{-1}
H^+	0	SO_4^{2-}	−216·9	Zn^{2+}	−36·4
OH^-	−54·6	NO_3^-	−49·4	Cd^{2+}	−17·3
F^-	−78·7	CO_3^{2-}	−161·6	Ca^{2+}	−129·8
Cl^-	−40·0	NH_4^+	−31·7	Cu^{2+}	15·4
Br^-	−28·9	Na^+	−57·3	Ag^+	25·3
I^-	−13·4	K^+	−60·0		

Problem 4.1

Calculate the enthalpy changes for the following reactions in dilute aqueous solution at 298°K.

(*a*) $HBr(aq) + NaCl(aq) \rightleftharpoons HCl(aq) + NaBr(aq)$
(*b*) $AgNO_3(aq) + NaCl(aq) \rightleftharpoons AgCl(s) + NaNO_3(aq)$
(*c*) $CaCl_2(aq) + K_2CO_3(aq) \rightleftharpoons CaCO_3(s) + 2KCl(aq)$
(*d*) $Na(s) + \tfrac{1}{2}Cl_2(g) + aq \rightleftharpoons Na^+(aq) + Cl^-(aq)$
(*e*) $2NH_4Cl(aq) + Na_2CO_3(aq) \rightleftharpoons (NH_4)_2CO_3(aq) + 2NaCl(aq)$

Use the data in table 4.3.

$$\Delta H^0_{f\,298}(AgCl(s)) = -30{\cdot}4\,\text{kcal mole}^{-1}$$
$$\Delta H^0_{f\,298}(CaCO_3(s)) = -288{\cdot}4\,\text{kcal mole}^{-1}$$

Problem 4.2

Calculate ΔH_{298} for the reaction

$$CdSO_4.H_2O(s) \rightleftharpoons CdSO_4(s) + H_2O(g)$$

using the following data relevant at 298°K.

$$CdSO_4(s) + 500\,H_2O(l) \rightleftharpoons CdSO_4 \text{ in } 500\,H_2O \qquad \Delta H = -11{\cdot}0\,\text{kcal}$$
$$CdSO_4.H_2O(s) + 499\,H_2O(l) \rightleftharpoons CdSO_4 \text{ in } 500\,H_2O \qquad \Delta H = -6{\cdot}1\,\text{kcal}$$
$$H_2O(l) \rightleftharpoons H_2O(g) \qquad \Delta H = +9{\cdot}7\,\text{kcal}$$

Energy and Ionic Equilibria

Historically, the distinction between weak and strong electrolytes was based on measurements of the conductivity of their solutions and the variation in conductivity with concentration. In this section a general appreciation of this distinction and its role in ionic equilibria is assumed. In its simplest form the dissociation of an electrolyte BA may be represented in general by the equation

$$BA \rightleftharpoons B^{+} + A^{-} \tag{21}$$

for which the equilibrium constant is written conventionally as

$$K = \frac{[B^{+}][A^{-}]}{[BA]} \tag{22}$$

For strong electroytes in dilute solution the concentration of the species BA at equilibrium [BA] is effectively zero. This corresponds to an infinitely large value of K with an associated infinitely negative value of the standard free energy change ΔG^0.

For weak electrolytes K has a finite value, usually considerably less than unity, the corresponding value of ΔG^0 being positive. The classification of electrolytes in the binary terminology of weak and strong is a rather restrictive one, while the variation of K from very large to very small values, e.g. $10^{+\infty}$ to $10^{-\infty}$, and in the corresponding values of ΔG^0 is continuous.

We are often content to express ionic equilibria simply in terms of values of K and to manipulate these values as such, rather than to discuss the equilibria in terms of free energies in the manner outlined in the earlier chapters for reactions not involving solutions. One reason for this is that we are much less concerned with the variation of K with temperature, and a second (and possibly more important one) is that there are some complexities in defining standard states. A particular problem in aqueous solutions is that we cannot have a single ionic species present, but must satisfy the condition of electrical neutrality.

Before considering another approach to this problem there is one important case in which the variation of K with temperature affords a useful confirmation of our discussion on heat of neutralization. The dissociation of water may be represented by the equation

$$H_2O(l) \rightleftharpoons H^+(aq) + OH^-(aq) \tag{23}$$

for which K is conventionally written

$$K = \frac{[H^+][OH^-]}{[H_2O]} \tag{24}$$

Since the dissociation is very small $[H_2O]$ is effectively constant at 55·5 mole l^{-1} and a new constant K_w, *the ionic product* for water, may be defined by

$$K_w = [H^+][OH^-] \tag{25}$$

There are several accurate experimental methods by which K_w may be measured over a range of temperatures. The results are shown in table 4.4.

TABLE 4.4: IONIC PRODUCT FOR WATER AT VARIOUS TEMPERATURES

Temperature °K	273	283	298	313	323
$K_w \times 10^{14}$	0·113	0·292	1·008	2·917	5·474

We recall from chapter 3 that the variation of an equilibrium constant with temperature is related to the enthalpy change for a reaction by the van't Hoff equation

$$\frac{d \ln K}{dT} = \frac{\Delta H}{RT^2} \tag{26}$$

which on integration gives

$$\log K_w = -\frac{H\Delta}{2{\cdot}303RT} + \text{constant} \tag{27}$$

The plot of $\log K_w$ against $1/T$ gives a value for ΔH of 13·8 kcal in good agreement with that of 13·7 kcal obtained calorimetrically.

Problem 4.3

The values for the ionization constant for aqueous NH_4OH solutions at the several temperatures noted are as follows:

T°K	273	283	293	303
$K_b \times 10^5$	4·862	4·804	4·767	4·724

Determine graphically the average enthalpy change accompanying the ionization of NH_4OH over this temperature range.

Electromotive Force and Free Energy

Consider first the reaction

$$\tfrac{1}{2}H_2(g)+AgCl(s) \rightleftharpoons Ag(s)+H^+ +Cl^- \tag{28}$$

in a solution of HCl. There will be for any such reaction a standard free energy change which we could in principle calculate if we knew the standard free energies of formation of all the reactants and products. Let us, however, use another approach foreshadowed in the last section. The reaction could be treated as the sum of two reactions

$$\tfrac{1}{2}H_2(g) \rightleftharpoons H^+ +e \tag{29}$$

$$AgCl(s)+e \rightleftharpoons Ag(s)+Cl^- \tag{30}$$

and instead of seeking to attribute standard free energies of formation individually to reactants and products, we could think of attributing a standard free energy change to each of these elementary reactions. If such a procedure were followed, it would be possible to list these values for a variety of such elementary reactions from which, by simple addition and subtraction, the standard free energy change of many complete reactions could be calculated. The first problem is to examine how the standard free energy change for reactions of the type (28) may be determined.

In the simple electrochemical cell shown in figure 4.1 hydrogen at 1 atm pressure is bubbled around the platinized platinum electrode A, while the other electrode B is a silver wire coated with AgCl. The electrolyte is HCl at a concentration of 1 mole per litre. If A and B are connected through a resistor, an electrical current flows, i.e. there is a passage of electrons through the resistor. This current results from the two chemical reactions—one in which electrons are released at one electrode, and one in which they are taken up at the other. These two processes are represented by equations (29) and (30) for the left-hand and right-hand electrodes, respectively, illustrated in figure 4.1.

The difference in the electrical potential between the electrodes, called the *electromotive force* and abbreviated emf, arises because the reaction at one electrode has a greater tendency to give up electrons than has the reaction at the other electrode.

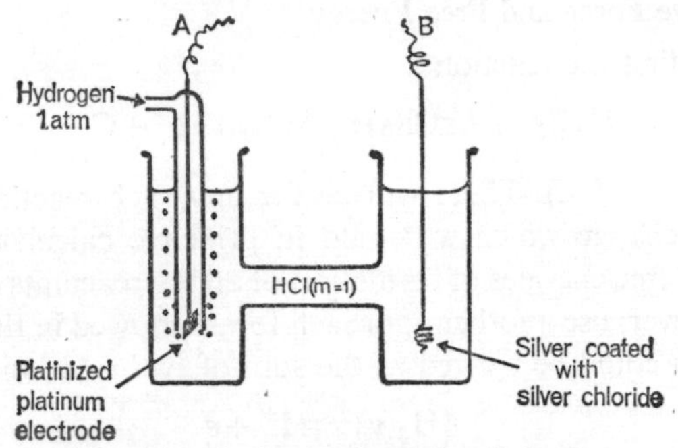

Fig. 4.1. A simple electrochemical cell

In chapter 2 a distinction was drawn between the energy change which occurred when a reaction actually proceeded and the free energy change which measured the potential or the capacity of a reaction to proceed. If, therefore, we could measure the emf under conditions in which no current flowed in the external circuit, we would be making a direct measurement of the free energy change for the reaction. This presents no practical difficulty, since all that is required is the application by means of an external potentiometer of a measured opposing emf just sufficient to balance that existing between the two electrodes. Under these conditions there is no current flow in the external circuit.

In this example if all the reactants and products are specified as being in their standard states (Ag(s), AgCl(s), HCl at unit concentration* and H_2 at 1 atm pressure), the measured equilibrium emf is the

* Strictly speaking, this should be defined in terms of unit activities of the H^+ and Cl^- ions which do not correspond accurately with unit concentrations. For simplicity the activity concept is not here introduced.

standard emf for the overall cell reaction (28). It is represented by E^0 and is expressed in volts. Our remaining task is to convert this emf in volts to more familiar energy units for the reaction represented by equation (28). To do this we need to multiply the measured value of E^0 in volts by the quantity of electrical charge corresponding to the molar quantities in the balanced equation as written. This quantity of charge is given by nF where n is the number of electrons transferred in the reaction as written and F is the Faraday, i.e. 96,500 coulombs (amperes × seconds). In our example n is clearly equal to unity.

The relationship between E^0 and the standard free energy change ΔG^0 is

$$\Delta G^0 = -nE^0F \tag{31}$$

but it is to be noted that, if E^0 is in volts and F in coulombs, the units of ΔG^0 will be joules and will need to be divided by 4·184 to convert the answer to calories.

In the cited example all the reactants and products were specified in their standard states and the measured emf was in consequence a standard emf E^0 with a corresponding standard free energy change ΔG^0. It is not, however, always convenient to have all the reactants and products in their respective standard states and for such cases the measured emf E is again related to the corresponding free energy change ΔG by an equation of similar form, namely

$$\Delta G = -nEF \tag{32}$$

As a matter of practical utility we shall need to know the relationship between ΔG and ΔG^0, i.e. between E and E^0.

For a general reaction

$$a\text{A} + b\text{B} \rightleftharpoons c\text{C} + d\text{D} \tag{33}$$

the relationship between ΔG and ΔG^0 takes the form

$$\Delta G = \Delta G^0 + RT \ln \frac{[\text{C}]^c[\text{D}]^d}{[\text{A}]^a[\text{B}]^b} \tag{34}$$

where the terms in square brackets represent concentrations of the respective reactants or products. Substitution of (31) and (32) in (34) yields

$$E = E^0 - \frac{RT}{nF} \ln \frac{[C]^c[D]^d}{[A]^a[B]^b} \tag{35}$$

which is commonly called the *Nernst equation.*

For the particular reaction (28) E will be given by

$$E = E^0 - \frac{RT}{F} \ln \frac{[Ag(s)][H^+][Cl^-]}{[AgCl(s)][H_2]^{\frac{1}{2}}} \tag{36}$$

Standard Electrode Potentials

The example discussed in the preceding section illustrates how the value of E^0 and hence ΔG^0 may be found directly by constructing a suitable electrochemical cell. Rather than tabulate values of E^0 and ΔG^0 for numerous complete reactions, and having in mind our basic aim to obtain the maximum amount of information from the minimum experimental effort, it would be more convenient if we could make a list of half reactions with their corresponding value of ΔG^0, so that a large variety of complete reactions could be formulated and the standard free energy changes calculated.

To do this we express the standard emf of the cell E^0_{cell} as

$$E^0_{cell} = E^0_{right} - E^0_{left} \tag{37}$$

where E^0_{right} and E^0_{left} are called the standard electrode potential of the two half-cells. We cannot, however, measure single electrode potentials in absolute terms, so that we again adopt the device of choosing one electrode as the reference electrode and attribute to that an $E^0_{electrode}$ value of zero. By convention this is the *standard hydrogen electrode*, abbreviated S.H.E., shown as the left-hand electrode in figure 4.1. For the example cited, the measured value of E^0_{cell} at 25°C is 0·2225 V and according to our convention E^0_{left} is zero; the standard electrode potential for the Ag/AgCl/Cl$^-$ electrode is therefore 0·2225 V. This means that for the half-cell reaction

$$\tfrac{1}{2}H_2(g) \rightleftharpoons H^+ + e \qquad E^0 = 0, \quad \Delta G^0 = 0 \tag{38}$$

and for the half-cell reaction

$$AgCl(s)+e \rightleftharpoons Ag(s)+Cl^- \qquad E^0 = 0{\cdot}2225\,V, \quad \Delta G^0 = -5132\,cal \qquad (39)$$

Table 4.5. gives a limited list of standard electrode potentials and corresponding standard free energy changes for the half-cell reactions. These reactions are expressed with the electron on the left-hand side of the equation. If a reaction is written in the opposite direction, the signs of the corresponding values of E^0 and ΔG^0 are of course reversed.

TABLE 4.5: STANDARD ELECTRODE POTENTIALS AND FREE ENERGY CHANGES AT 25°C

Half-cell reaction	E^0 volt	ΔG^0 kcal
$Li^+ + e \rightleftharpoons Li$	$-3{\cdot}045$	70·24
$Na^+ + e \rightleftharpoons Na$	$-2{\cdot}714$	62·59
$\frac{1}{3}Al_3{}^+ + e \rightleftharpoons \frac{1}{3}Al$	$-1{\cdot}66$	38·3
$\frac{1}{2}Zn^{2+} + e \rightleftharpoons \frac{1}{2}Zn$	$-0{\cdot}763$	17·59
$\frac{1}{2}Fe^{2+} + e \rightleftharpoons \frac{1}{2}Fe$	$-0{\cdot}440$	10·15
$Cr_3{}^+ + e \rightleftharpoons Cr^{2+}$	$-0{\cdot}41$	9·5
$\frac{1}{2}PbBr_2 + e \rightleftharpoons \frac{1}{2}Pb + Br^-$	$-0{\cdot}280$	6·46
$AgI + e \rightleftharpoons Ag + I^-$	$-0{\cdot}151$	3·48
$\frac{1}{2}Pb^{2+} + e \rightleftharpoons \frac{1}{2}Pb$	$-0{\cdot}126$	2·91
$H^+ + e \rightleftharpoons \frac{1}{2}H_2$	0·000	0
$Cu^{2+} + e \rightleftharpoons Cu^+$	$+0{\cdot}153$	$-3{\cdot}53$
$AgCl + e \rightleftharpoons Ag + Cl^-$	$+0{\cdot}2225$	$-5{\cdot}132$
$\frac{1}{2}Hg_2Cl_2 + e \rightleftharpoons Hg+Cl^-$	$+0{\cdot}268$	$-6{\cdot}18$
$Cu^+ + e \rightleftharpoons Cu$	$+0{\cdot}521$	$-12{\cdot}01$
$Fe_3{}^+ + e \rightleftharpoons Fe^{2+}$	$+0{\cdot}771$	$-17{\cdot}78$
$Ag^+ + e \rightleftharpoons Ag$	$+0{\cdot}7991$	$-18{\cdot}43$
$\frac{1}{2}Cl_2(g) + e \rightleftharpoons Cl^-$	$+1{\cdot}3595$	$-31{\cdot}35$
$\frac{1}{2}PbO_2 + 2H^+ + e \rightleftharpoons \frac{1}{2}Pb^{2+} + H_2O$	$+1{\cdot}455$	$-33{\cdot}56$
$\frac{1}{3}Au^{3+} + e \rightleftharpoons \frac{1}{3}Au$	$+1{\cdot}50$	$-34{\cdot}6$
$Ce^{4+} + e \rightleftharpoons Ce^{3+}$	$+1{\cdot}61$	$-37{\cdot}1$
$H^+ + \frac{1}{2}F_2 + e \rightleftharpoons HF aq$	$+3{\cdot}06$	$-70{\cdot}6$

We shall illustrate the use of such a table by a few examples. Consider the reaction

$$Zn(s)+CuSO_4(aq) \rightleftharpoons ZnSO_4(aq)+Cu(s) \qquad (40)$$

Since $ZnSO_4$ and $CuSO_4$ are both salts they will in aqueous solution be fully ionized, and we may first simplify the equation by eliminating the SO_4^{2-} ion from both sides of the equation, leaving

$$Zn(s) + Cu^{2+} \rightleftharpoons Zn^{2+} + Cu(s) \tag{41}$$

From table 4.5

$$\tfrac{1}{2}Zn^{2+} + e \rightleftharpoons \tfrac{1}{2}Zn(s) \qquad \Delta G^0 = 17{,}590\,\text{cal} \tag{42}$$

$$Cu^{2+} + e \rightleftharpoons Cu^{+} \qquad \Delta G^0 = -3530\,\text{cal} \tag{43}$$

$$Cu^{+} + e \rightleftharpoons Cu(s) \qquad \Delta G^0 = -12{,}010\,\text{cal} \tag{44}$$

By adding (43) and (44) and by multiplying (42) by 2 and inverting we have

$$Cu^{2+} + 2e \rightleftharpoons Cu(s) \qquad \Delta G^0 = -3530 - 12{,}010 = -15{,}540\,\text{cal} \tag{45}$$

$$Zn(s) \rightleftharpoons Zn^{2+} + 2e \qquad \Delta G^0 = -2 \times 17{,}590 = -35{,}180\,\text{cal} \tag{46}$$

Addition of (45) and (46) yields

$$Zn(s) + Cu^{2+} \rightleftharpoons Zn^{2+} + Cu(s) \qquad \Delta G^0 = -50{,}720\,\text{cal} \tag{47}$$

from which it is evident that the equilibrium constant is large and the reaction as written may proceed virtually to completion from left to right. In a similar way, the standard free energy change and hence the equilibrium constant may be calculated for any reaction for which the necessary data are available.

These data may also be used to calculate the solubility products of sparingly soluble salts. This we shall illustrate in the case of AgI for which the solubility product K_{sp} is the equilibrium constant for the reaction

$$AgI(s) \rightleftharpoons Ag^{+} + I^{-} \tag{48}$$

This may be obtained from the two half-cell reactions

$$AgI(s) + e \rightleftharpoons Ag(s) + I^{-} \qquad \Delta G^0 = 3480\,\text{cal} \tag{49}$$

$$Ag^{+} + e \rightleftharpoons Ag(s) \qquad \Delta G^0 = -18{,}430\,\text{cal} \tag{50}$$

Subtraction of (50) from (49) results in equation (48) for which

$$\Delta G^0 = 3480-(-18{,}430) = 21{,}910$$
$$= -RT \ln K_{sp} \qquad (51)$$

whence

$$\log K_{sp} = -\frac{21{,}910}{2{\cdot}303 \times 1{\cdot}99 \times 298} = -16{\cdot}0 \qquad (52)$$

The point to be noted here is that table 4.5 is no more than a table of standard free energy changes for half-reactions relative to the standard free energy change for the half-reaction

$$H^+ + e \rightleftharpoons \tfrac{1}{2}H_2(g) \qquad (53)$$

arbitrarily taken as zero. We could, of course, have chosen any other convenient half-reaction as the arbitrary zero, since for any complete reaction we are concerned with the difference between the recorded values of ΔG^0 for two half-reactions. Electrochemical cells are simply a practical means of obtaining free energy changes for reactions and not in our present context an end in themselves. Compared with our discussion in earlier chapters, we have simply chosen a different, and in this case more convenient, way of splitting up ΔG^0 for a complete reaction (the only quantity of experimental significance) into two components each representing a half-reaction, instead of attributing values to individual reactants or products.

Problem 4.4

Using the data in table 4.5, write down the appropriate half-cell reactions and calculate the values of ΔG^0_{298} for the following reactions:

(*a*) $2Ag(s) + Cu(NO_3)_2(aq) \rightleftharpoons 2AgNO_3(aq) + Cu(s)$

(*b*) $2FeSO_4(aq) + 2Ce(SO_4)_2(aq) \rightleftharpoons Fe_2(SO_4)_3(aq) + Ce_2(SO_4)_3(aq)$

(*c*) $Hg_2Cl_2(s) + H_2(g) \rightleftharpoons 2Hg(l) + 2HCl(aq)$

(*d*) $Zn(s) + 2HCl(aq) \rightleftharpoons ZnCl_2(aq) + H_2(g)$

Problem 4.5

An iron (II) sulphate solution, 0·01 molar, is mixed with an equal volume of a cerium (IV) nitrate solution of the same concentration at 25°C. Calculate the equilibrium concentration of the iron (III) ion in the solution.

Problem 4.6

Calculate the solubility product of AgCl at 25°C.

Entropy and Enthalpy Changes for Ionic Reactions in Solution

If the equilibrium constant for a reaction can be determined at more than one temperature, ΔH^0 may in general be calculated using one of the integrated forms of the van't Hoff equation

$$\frac{d \ln K}{dT} = \frac{\Delta H^0}{RT^2} \tag{26}$$

For many reactions this is not a very accurate method of determining ΔH^0 because of the logarithmic function involved. In ionic systems in which ΔG^0 and K can be determined from measurements of E^0, this disadvantage is less serious, since E^0 can often be determined with considerable accuracy. Measurement of E^0 and the temperature coefficient of E^0 would enable ΔH^0 to be determined by the use of equation (26).

It is, however, convenient to employ an alternative form which makes use of a relationship not introduced hitherto, namely

$$\left(\frac{\partial \Delta G^0}{\partial T}\right)_P = -\Delta S^0 \tag{54}$$

If we also recall equations

$$\Delta G^0 = -nE^0F \tag{31}$$

and

$$\Delta G^0 = \Delta H^0 - T\Delta S^0 \tag{55}$$

it follows by substitution that

$$-nE^0F = \Delta H^0 - nFT\left(\frac{\partial E^0}{\partial T}\right)_P \tag{56}$$

whence

$$\Delta H^0 = -nE^0F + nFT\left(\frac{\partial E^0}{\partial T}\right)_P \tag{57}$$

Substitution of E^0 and the temperature coefficient of E^0 in (57) gives directly the values for ΔH^0.

We may illustrate this with reference to the reaction

$$Cd(s)+Hg_2SO_4(s)+\tfrac{8}{3}H_2O(l)\rightleftharpoons CdSO_4.\tfrac{8}{3}H_2O(s)+2Hg(l) \quad (58)$$

which is the cell reaction for the Weston standard cell. At 25°C, $E^0 = 1{\cdot}01463$ volt and $dE^0/dT = -5{\cdot}00 \times 10^{-5}$ volt deg^{-1} whence for this reaction

$$\Delta G^0_{298} = -\frac{2\times 96{,}500\times 1{\cdot}01463}{4{\cdot}184} = -46{,}800\,\text{cal}$$

$$\Delta S^0_{298} = \frac{2\times 96{,}500\times(-5{\cdot}00\times 10^{-5})}{4{\cdot}184} = -2{\cdot}31\,\text{cal deg}^{-1}$$

$$\Delta H^0_{298} = -46{,}800-690 = -47{,}490\,\text{cal}$$

In this chapter we have made considerable use of the existence of ions in electrolytic solutions. It should, however, be remembered that what we can measure electrochemically are the values of ΔH^0, ΔS^0, and ΔG^0 for a complete reaction and that these values depend on the initial state (the reactants) and the final state (the products) as defined by the balanced chemical reaction, and do not involve detailed ideas on the nature of the solutions or of any particular mechanism. The concept of ions is introduced into the thermodynamic discussion to make use of information about solutions obtained from non-equilibrium studies of various kinds, e.g. conductivity, diffusion, or from purely theoretical models.

Problem 4.7

An electrochemical cell was set up in which the following reaction could be studied:

$$2H_2S(g) + Mo(s) \rightleftharpoons 2H_2(g) + MoS_2(s)$$

The values of the standard emf measured at 288 and 308°K were, respectively, 0·4148 and 0·4087 volt.

(*a*) Calculate the standard free energy change and equilibrium constant at 298°K.

(*b*) Calculate the average standard enthalpy change for the reaction over the range 288–308°K.

(*c*) Calculate the standard entropy change for the reaction at 298°K.

5

ENERGY RELATIONSHIPS IN THE PERIODIC CLASSIFICATION

Historically, the periodic classification of the elements had its origins in the recognition by Lothar Meyer, Mendeleef, and others that elements arranged in increasing order of atomic weight displayed a number of periodic similarities in physical and chemical properties. With the development of the modern periodic classification based on atomic numbers and related to the configuration and energy distribution of the extra-nuclear electrons, we have come to the stage of emphasizing these models introduced to explain the difference in physical properties and chemical behaviour almost to the exclusion of the quantitative description of the macro properties. In this chapter we shall examine how the energy concepts introduced in earlier chapters afford a means of redressing the balance.

Physical Properties

Considerable attention has been given in textbooks to examining the trends in melting and boiling points and of the heats of fusion and vaporization of the elements in relation to the periodic classification. These concepts emphasize certain comparatively isolated organizational features and the temperatures and energy changes associated with changes from one form of aggregation to another. We shall take a rather broader view and begin by reiterating the relationship

$$H = G + TS \tag{1}$$

where H has been called the total energy, G the free energy, and TS the fixed or organizational energy. It will be recalled that neither H nor

G can be evaluated absolutely for individual elements or compounds, but that the entropy S may be determined absolutely from experimental measurements of the heat capacity from near 0°K to the temperature of interest. In the organizational energy TS we have a quantitative measure of the way in which the component atoms, ions, or molecules in elements or compounds are ordered.

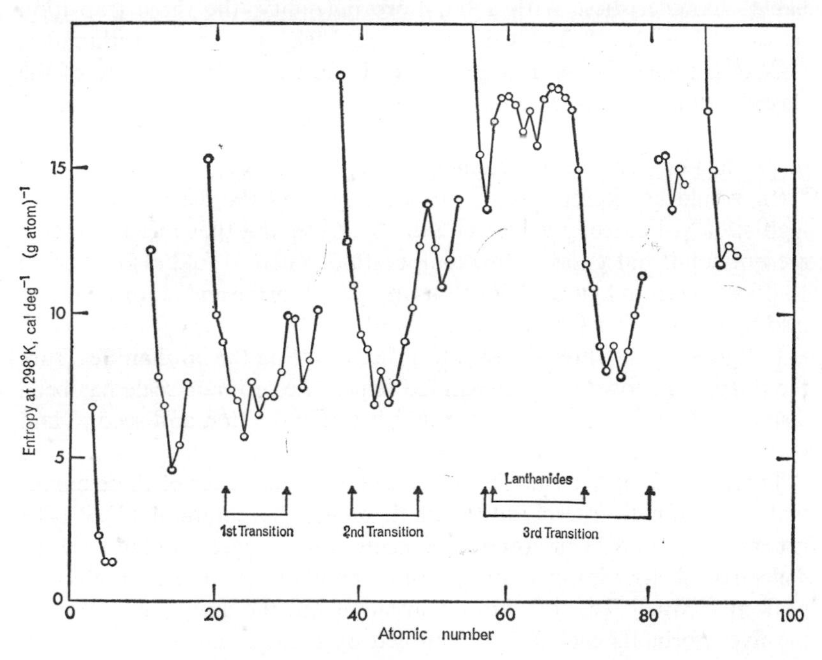

Fig. 5.1. Standard entropies at 298°K for the solid elements

For some particular temperature, e.g. 298°K, TS for the elements will be proportional to the entropy S; it will serve our purposes if we examine the values of S for the elements at 298°K for which data are conveniently available. For the moment attention is directed to the 78 elements which are solids at 298°K; in figure 5.1 the standard entropies S^0 for these elements at this temperature and 1 atmosphere pressure are plotted against the atomic number.

With a few exceptions most of the values lie between 5 and 30 cal deg^{-1} $(g\,atom)^{-1}$ with some evidence of a trend to higher values with increasing atomic number. There is from figure 5.1 little difficulty in defining the main periods, of identifying groups I and II, of recognizing the existence of the short and long periods, and of noting the existence of a $2n^2$ relationship (8, 18, 32, etc.) from the successive occurrence of identifiable characteristics. With a bit more ingenuity, the three transition series ^{21}Sc–^{30}Zn, ^{39}Y–^{48}Cd and ^{57}La–^{80}Hg and the lanthanides, ^{58}Ce–^{71}Lu may also be recognized. In brief, the main structure of the classification emerges from this figure.

There are also a number of predictions which can be made from the diagram. For example, the elements ^{2}He, ^{10}Ne, ^{18}Ar, ^{36}Kr, ^{54}Xe, and ^{86}Rn would be expected (by extrapolating from the diagram) to have high standard entropy values at 298°K, suggesting that these elements are not solids but gases at this temperature. There would also be some justification from figure 5.1 for thinking that fluorine and chlorine might also be gases at this temperature.

In figure 5.2 the three transition series, omitting the lanthanides from the third, are shown on an expanded scale. The ordinate scale has been displaced by 2·5 cal deg^{-1} $(g\ atom)^{-1}$ between the first and second and between the second and third series.

There can be little doubt from the repetitive character of these curves that the ultimate interpretation of them will be common to all. The general shape may be interpreted in terms of the progressive filling of the *d*-electron shells with increasing atomic number, and the characteristic peak at ^{25}Mn, ^{43}Tc, and ^{75}Re as arising from the unique situation of the five *d*-orbitals each being occupied by a single unpaired electron. Further, we may note that this feature is progressively rather less pronounced as the principal quantum number of the *d*-electrons increases.

An important point here is that this particular explanation is in terms of an electron model which is quite independent of the observed entropy values. What we can say is that this explanation is in accord with the observed properties as measured and defined by these entropy values.

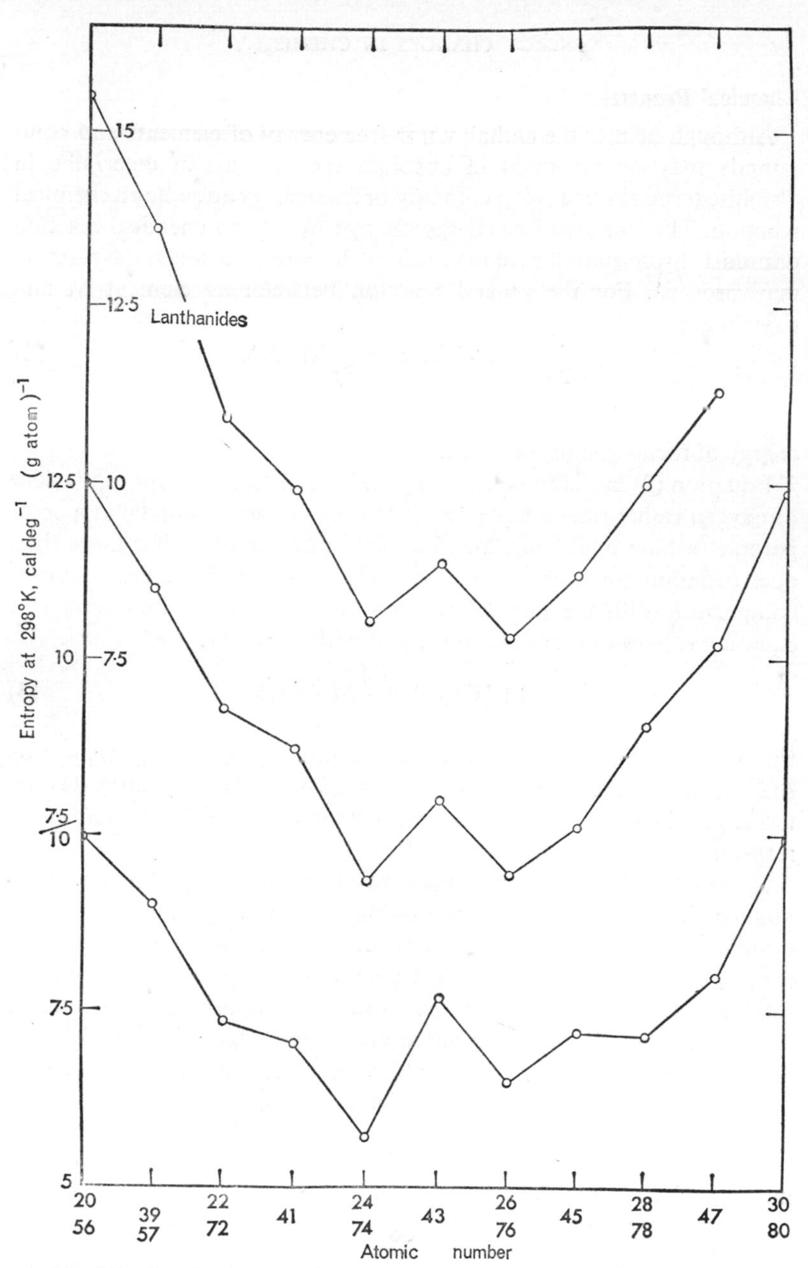

Fig. 5.2. Standard entropies at 298°K for elements of the transition series

Chemical Properties

Although neither the enthalpy nor free energy of elements and compounds may be measured in absolute terms, we can determine in absolute terms the change in enthalpy or free energy attending a chemical reaction. The standard free energy change ΔG^0 for a chemical reaction affords a direct quantitative measure of the extent to which the reaction may proceed. For the general reaction between an element M and oxygen gas

$$\frac{x}{2y}\,M(s)+\tfrac{1}{4}O_2(g) \rightleftharpoons \frac{1}{2y}\,M_xO_y(s) \tag{2}$$

the value of ΔG^0 at a particular temperature is equal to standard free energy of formation of the oxide.

Equation (2) has been deliberately written in terms of one equivalent of oxygen rather than a mole or a g atom, in order to handle in a comparable fashion oxides in which the element M may exhibit more than one oxidation state, and more particularly, to permit more adequate comparison with the parallel reaction with chlorine—represented in equation (3)—with other halogens, and with nitrogen:

$$\frac{x}{y}M(s)+\tfrac{1}{2}Cl_2(g) \rightleftharpoons \frac{1}{y}M_xCl_y(s) \tag{3}$$

For such reactions we may write the standard free energy change as ΔG^0_{eq} to indicate this fact and, if we need them, by similarly defined terms for the standard enthalpy and entropy changes, ΔH^0_{eq} and ΔS^0_{eq}, respectively.

Since ΔG^0_{eq} gives directly a measure of the stability of binary compounds of the type shown in equations (2) and (3), it is possible to examine the stabilities of such compounds over a wide range of positive elements for a number of negative components, e.g. nitrogen, oxygen, sulphur, and the halogens. For purposes of comparison, the choice of temperature will have little relative effect. A temperature of 298°K is used throughout, and the main effect of temperature over moderate ranges on the value of ΔG^0 may be assessed from the approximation

$$\Delta G^0_T \approx \Delta H^0_{298} - T\Delta S^0_{298} \tag{4}$$

introduced and discussed in chapter 3.

There are two additional problems. The first concerns the choice of oxidation state where more than one possibility exists. We may choose either (i) the state for which ΔG^0_{eq} has the lowest (i.e. largest negative) value, or (ii) the oxidation state given by the group in the Periodic Table in which the positive element falls, e.g. K_2O, CaO, Sc_2O_3, TiO_2, V_2O_5, CrO_3, Mn_2O_7. The former choice is more useful and realistic since it avoids the necessity of having advance knowledge of the Periodic Table in detailed form. The second problem arises for a few elements for which

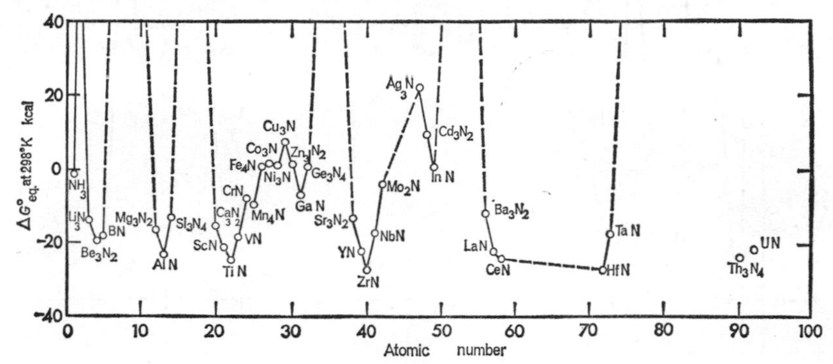

Fig. 5.3. Free energy spectra for nitrides

the states specified in equations (2) and (3) are not the stable states at 298°K and 1 atm pressure. Here we may either omit such cases from consideration altogether, or include them while recognizing that ΔS^0_{eq} and hence ΔG^0_{eq} for such compounds may be somewhat abnormal.

For the noble gases, we would until recently have attributed to any possible compounds of them large positive values of ΔG^0_{eq}. The fact that a number of such compounds, especially of Xe and F, have now been prepared and show considerable stability, must cause some revision of this assumption, but there is some advantage in maintaining it for the moment in order to see where it leads.

With these limitations and approximations, conveniently available data on the ΔG^0_{eq} as a function of the atomic number of the positive element are graphically shown in figures 5.3 (nitrides), 5.4 (oxides), 5.5 (fluorides), 5.6 (sulphides), 5.7 (chlorides), and 5.8 (bromides). If the plotted points are joined sequentially, the resulting diagrams may for convenience be termed *free energy spectra.*

In spite of the fragmentary nature of the data in some cases, it may readily be seen that the same general pattern applies throughout these groups of compounds with systematic variation in the free energy scale

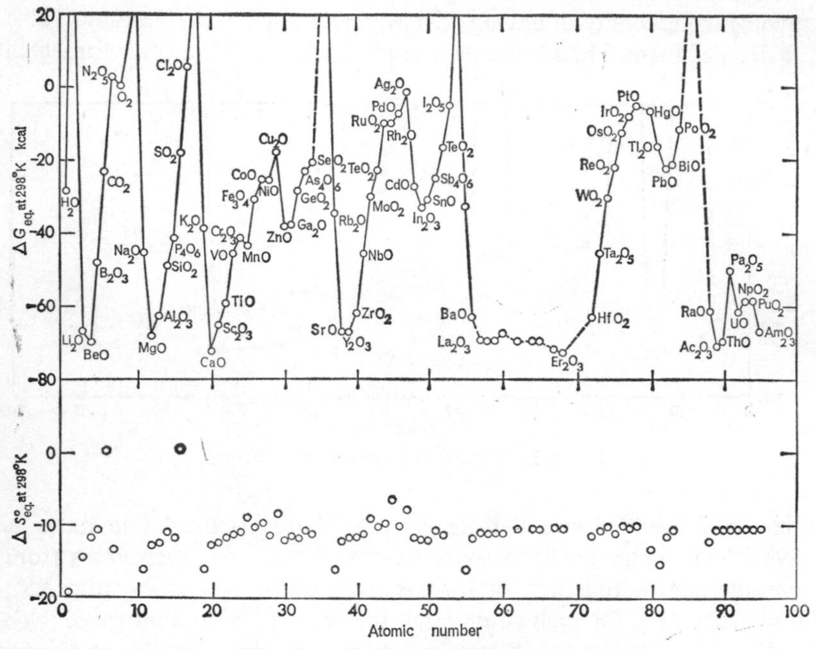

Fig. 5.4. Free energy spectra for oxides

across the periodic classification (nitride, oxide, fluoride), and down the classification (oxide, sulphide, and more particularly fluoride, chloride, bromide). Clearly, the stabilities increase across and decrease down the classification.

The gross structure of these spectra may be regarded as a series of stability valleys lying between the noble gases. The compounds of maximum stability at 298°K read from these graphs are set out in table 5.1.

TABLE 5.1: COMPOUNDS OF MAXIMUM STABILITY AT 298°K

Compound	Positive elements
Nitrides	Be, Al, Ti, Zn
Oxides	Be, Mg, Ca, Y, Sr
Fluorides	Li, Na, Ca, Sr, Ba
Chlorides	Li, Na, K, Rb, Ba
Bromides	Li, Na, K, Rb, Cs
Sulphides	Li, Na, Ca, Sr, Ba

The general shifts in the above table towards the alkali metals both across and down the periodic classification are evident. A survey of the valley depths for the several compounds relative to the respective component elements also serves to emphasize the quantitative trend across and down the classification. In round figures these are set out in table 5.2.

TABLE 5.2: DEPTH OF VALLEYS OF STABILITY AT 298°K

Nitride −25	Oxide −70	Fluoride −135
	Sulphide −60	Chloride −95
		Bromide −90

One of the consequences of these data concerns the possible stability of binary compounds of the noble gases. If such compounds are to be formed at all, the diagrams suggest that the fluorides should be considerably more stable than other compounds.

In the stability valleys associated with the long periods, i.e. Ar–Kr, Kr–Xe, and Xe–Rn, fine structure is developed and may be recognized in terms of the interpolation of the three transition series of elements and the lanthanides. The data on the oxides of the first transition series

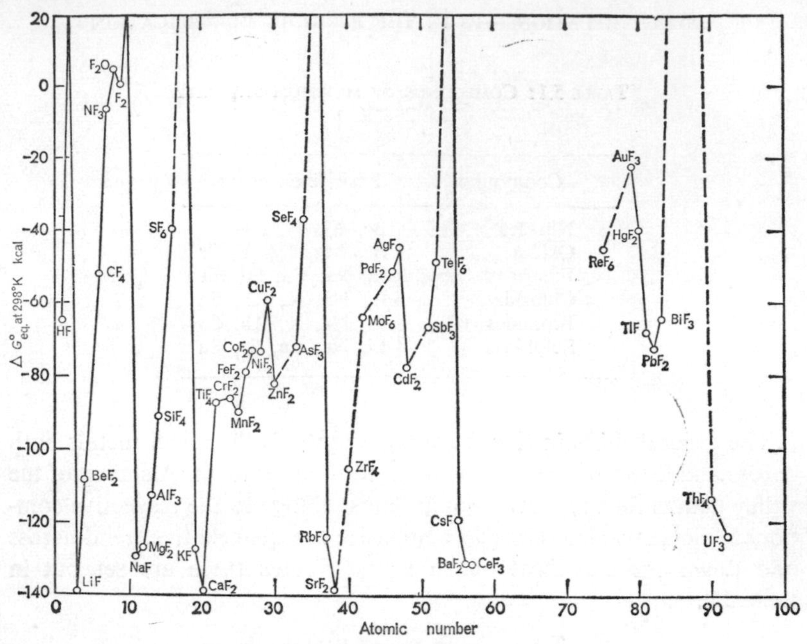

Fig. 5.5. Free energy spectra for fluorides

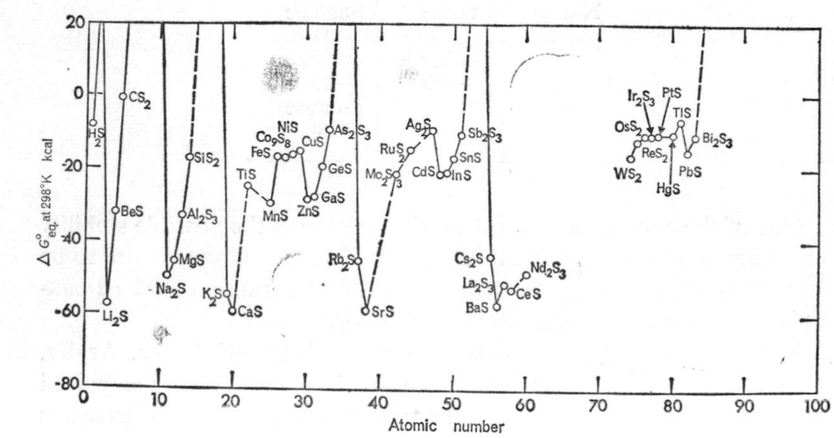

Fig. 5.6. Free energy spectra for sulphides

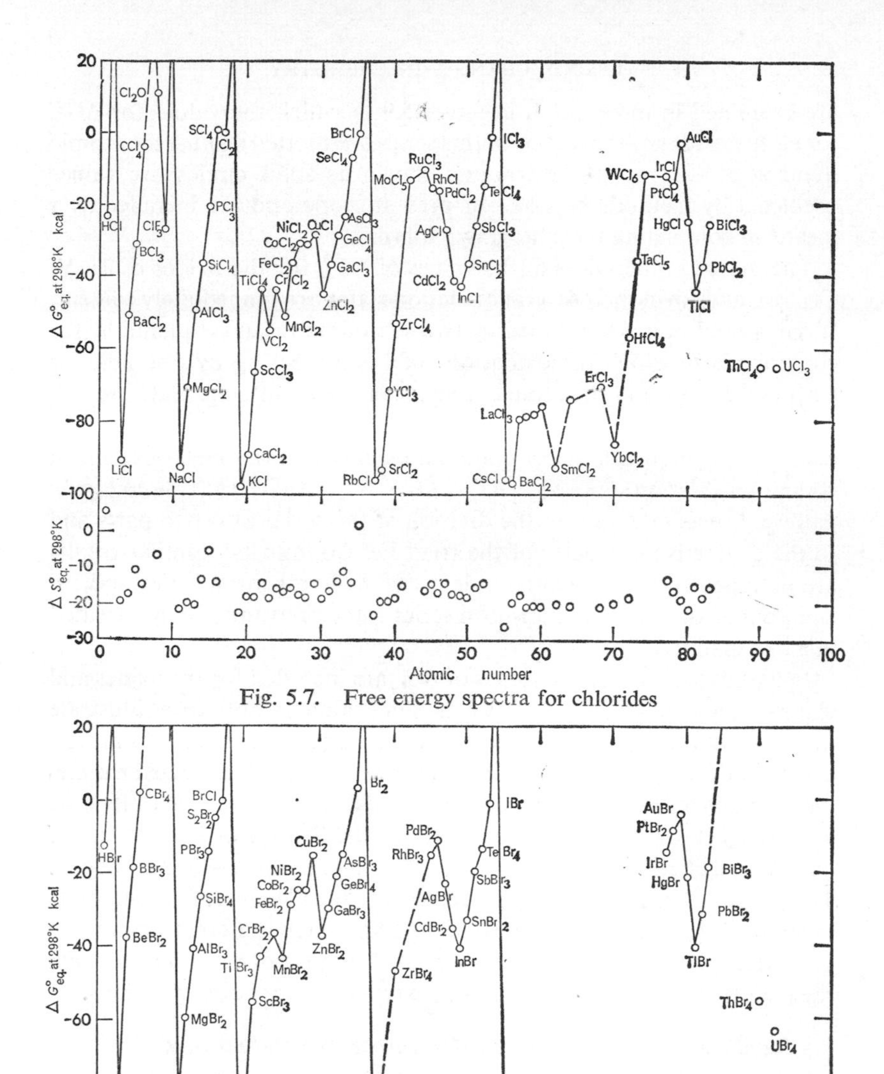

Fig. 5.7. Free energy spectra for chlorides

Fig. 5.8. Free energy spectra for bromides

are examined in more detail in figure 5.9 in which the values for ΔG^0_{eq} for all the oxides of the metals in this series are plotted against the atomic number of the metal. Two points shown as solid circles are values predicted by methods beyond our present scope and are included as a means of completing the emerging pattern.

The marked differences in the values of ΔG^0_{eq} for the oxides of Ti, V, Cr, Mn, and Fe in their several oxidation states are immediately evident. If the plotted points are joined by two sets of curves, (i) sequentially for compounds in which the oxidation state is increasing by one unit for each unit increase in the atomic number of the metal, e.g. CaO, Sc_2O_3, TiO_2, V_2O_5, CrO_3, etc., and Cu_2O, ZnO, Ga_2O_3, GeO_2, As_2O_5, SeO_3, etc., and (ii) sequentially for compounds in which the metal exhibits a common oxidation state, e.g. TiO_2, VO_2, CrO_2, MnO_2, etc., the emerging pattern directs attention to the division of the series into two parts and to the distinctive character of the triad Fe, Co, and Ni. Similar results are obtained for other compounds of the first transition series and for compounds of the other transition series if the relevant data are treated in a like manner.

In figures 5.4 and 5.7 the values of ΔS^0_{eq} are included for the oxides and chlorides, respectively. The fairly consistent values in both cases illustrate the fact that the entropy changes for reactions (2) and (3) are not greatly dependent on the particular positive element involved, provided the element and its oxide or chloride are both solids. Under these conditions we would expect ΔS^0_{eq} to arise principally from the fixation of 1 equivalent of oxygen and of chlorine, respectively, namely $-12{\cdot}2$ and $-26{\cdot}7$ cal deg^{-1}. The actual values are rather less than these predicted values. The few points in figures 5.4 and 5.7 showing values of ΔS^0_{eq} widely different from these general levels arise from the inclusion in the graphs of reactions in which the phases are not those specified in the two corresponding reactions.

(a) *Stability of sulphates, hydroxides, carbonates and nitrates*

The stability of these compounds may be defined in terms of the equivalent standard free energies of decomposition which, in the case of sulphates, refer to the reaction

$$\frac{1}{2y}\,M_x(SO_4)_y(s) \rightleftharpoons \frac{1}{2y}\,M_xO_y(s) + \tfrac{1}{2}SO_3(g) \qquad (5)$$

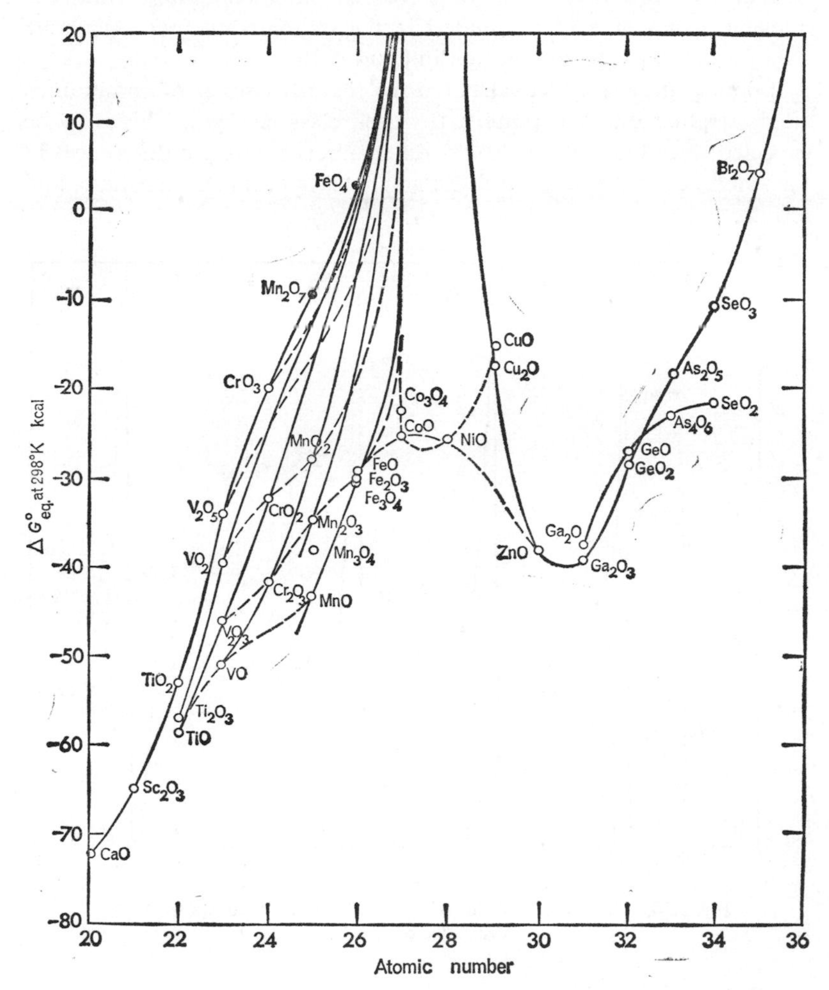

Fig. 5.9. Equivalent standard free energies of formation of the oxides of the first transition series at 298°K

Similar reactions may be written for the other compounds and the relevant values of ΔG^0_{eq} calculated in the standard manner. Available data for the sulphates are plotted in figure 5.10.

If similar graphs are constructed for the other series of compounds cited, a rather different pattern for each class emerges. This is to be expected since the pattern should reflect in each case the differences in the stabilities of the oxide and the sulphate, hydroxide, carbonate, and nitrate.

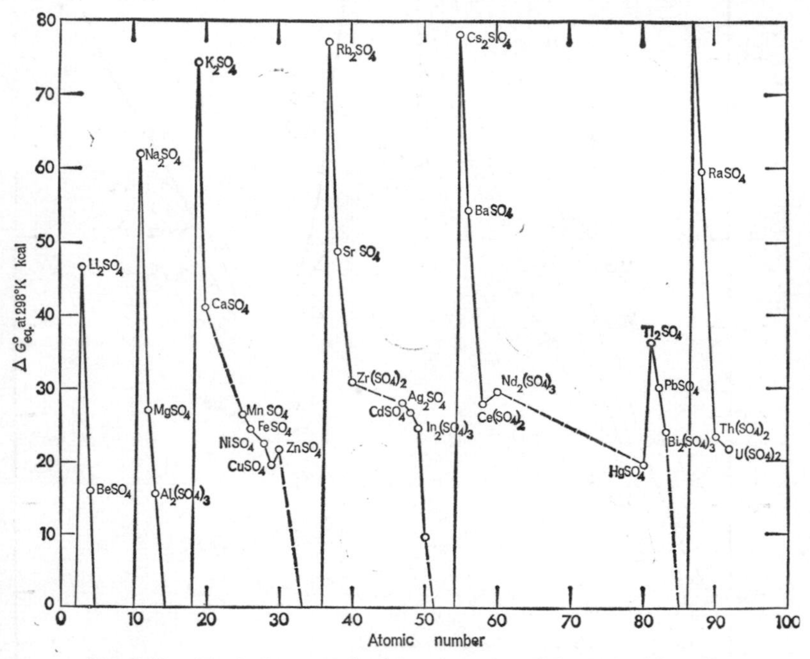

Fig. 5.10. Equivalent standard free energies of decomposition of sulphates at 298°K

(b) *Oxides of* C, N, Si, S

Considerable practical and theoretical interest attaches to the combination of these elements with oxygen and, in particular, to the prediction of the equilibria between different oxides of the same element at different temperatures. The implications of the equilibria between CO_2, CO, and O_2 in combustion processes is a simple example of significance.

An effective way of examining and illustrating the relevant free energy changes in these systems is in terms of an Ellingham diagram in which the standard free energy change is plotted against the temperature for the reactions between these elements and oxygen. Some examples on a slightly simplified basis are shown in figure 5.11 for which the relevant reactions are as follows:

$$Si(s)+O_2(g) \rightleftharpoons SiO_2(s) \quad (6)$$
$$2Si(s)+O_2(g) \rightleftharpoons 2SiO(g) \quad (7)$$
$$C(s)+O_2(g) \rightleftharpoons CO_2(g) \quad (8)$$
$$2C(s)+O_2(g) \rightleftharpoons 2CO(g) \quad (9)$$
$$2N_2(g)+O_2(g) \rightleftharpoons 2N_2O(g) \quad (10)$$
$$N_2(g)+O_2(g) \rightleftharpoons 2NO(g) \quad (11)$$
$$\tfrac{1}{2}N_2(g)+O_2(g) \rightleftharpoons NO_2(g) \quad (12)$$
$$\tfrac{1}{2}N_2(g)+O_2(g) \rightleftharpoons \tfrac{1}{2}N_2O_4(g) \quad (13)$$
$$S_2(g)+O_2(g) \rightleftharpoons 2SO(g) \quad (14)$$
$$\tfrac{1}{2}S_2(g)+O_2(g) \rightleftharpoons SO_2(g) \quad (15)$$
$$\tfrac{1}{3}S_2(g)+O_2(g) \rightleftharpoons \tfrac{2}{3}SO_3(g) \quad (16)$$

All the equations are written with respect to 1 mole of oxygen and, except in equations (6) and (7), uniformity in the states of reactants and products for each group of reactions has been attained to facilitate comparison.

The general order of increasing stabilities read off the graphs is clearly N, S, C, Si, the commonly recognized instability of the oxides of nitrogen being in stark contrast with the immense stability of SiO_2. For the oxides of nitrogen in all cases but one, namely the formation of NO, the standard free energy changes become increasingly large (and positive) as the temperature increases. The conditions for the formation of NO will clearly be favoured by the use of very high temperatures.

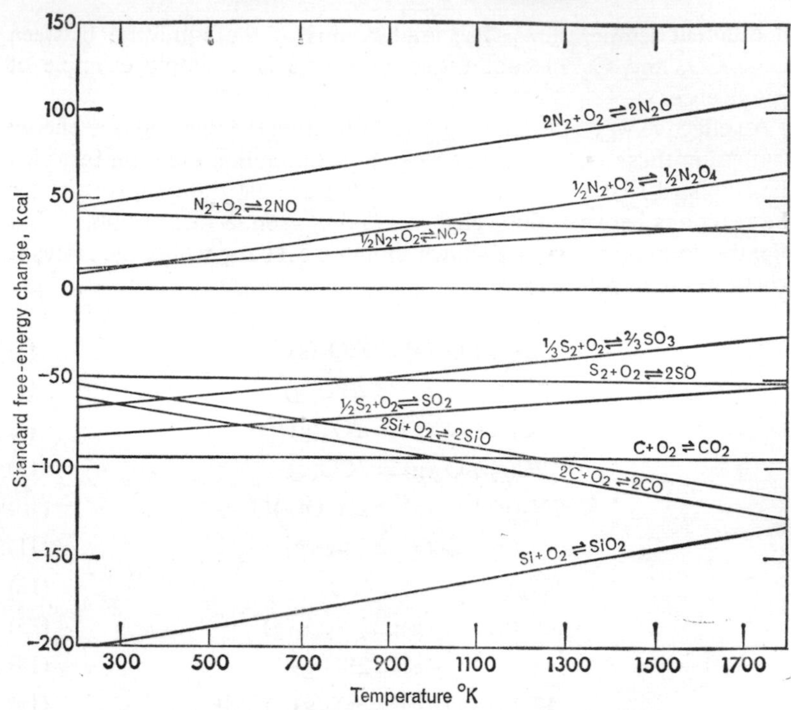

Fig. 5.11. Simplified Ellingham diagrams for the oxides of C, N, Si, and S

We may also note that the lines for equations (12) and (13) for the formation of NO_2 and $\frac{1}{2}N_2O_4$ respectively cross at about 300°K, the dimeric form being more stable at the lower, and the monomer at the higher temperatures. Subtraction of equation (13) from (12) yields

$$\tfrac{1}{2}N_2O_4(g) \rightleftharpoons NO_2 \tag{17}$$

and at the crossing point referred to ΔG^0 will be zero, i.e. the equilibrium constant expressed by the equation

$$K_p = \frac{p_{NO_2}}{(p_{N_2O_4})^{\frac{1}{2}}} \tag{18}$$

will be unity.

Similar considerations apply to the oxides of carbon for which it is evident from the diagram that CO_2 will be the preferred compound at temperatures below about 1200°K and CO favoured at temperatures above this value. Diagrams of this kind often permit the presentation of a large amount of information on the variation of the standard free energy change with temperature for reactions of a given type. They are much used to display information on equilibria in systems of metallurgical interest involving, for example, the formation of metal oxides, the roasting of metal sulphides, and the reduction of oxides with carbon monoxide or hydrogen.

The examples used in this chapter are illustrative and not exhaustive. The methods outlined clearly answer some questions, but perhaps their real value lies in the much larger number of questions they pose. One group of these is concerned with the nature of the chemical bonds in molecules, the subject of the next chapter.

6

ENERGY AND CHEMICAL BONDING

One of the important activities in chemistry is to seek to correlate the properties of chemical substances with their structure, that is to find answers to the questions of how the atoms are joined together to form molecules and how atoms, ions, or molecules are arranged in solids and liquids. There is now a variety of experimental methods available which enable us to find answers to some of these questions, but, as we cannot hope to examine every chemical substance in order to determine its structure individually, we would also like to know why particular structures are formed.

One of the most useful ways of approaching this problem is in terms of models, not necessarily physically realizable models, but often simply mental constructs, such as ionic and covalent bonds. If we can devise a model from which by using established theorems in, for example, geometry, mechanics, and electrostatics, the structure and properties of groups of substances can consistently be calculated in agreement with experimental observations, then a powerful prediction tool will be at hand. It has, however, seldom been possible to devise a model which would adequately describe simultaneously all the structural features and, not infrequently, several models each capable of dealing with one aspect have had to be employed.

It is essential to distinguish clearly between that which is observable, e.g. the energy change in a chemical reaction, and a model which affords an instructive though not necessarily unique way of describing a mechanism or correlating observed information or behaviour. For example, if we write down for ethylene the formula, $CH_2{=}CH_2$, the double covalent bond (a particular electronic model) predicts that, in the absence of other interfering factors, the chemical reactions of ethylene should be those which have been established as common in substances containing such bonds. What we seek to do in this chapter is to illustrate how measurable energy changes afford important criteria for testing proposed structural models.

Lattice Energy of Ionic Solids

When a salt such as NaCl is dissolved in water, many of the properties of the solution may be described in terms of the existence of equal numbers of Na^+ ions and Cl^- ions. Either NaCl dissolves to yield NaCl

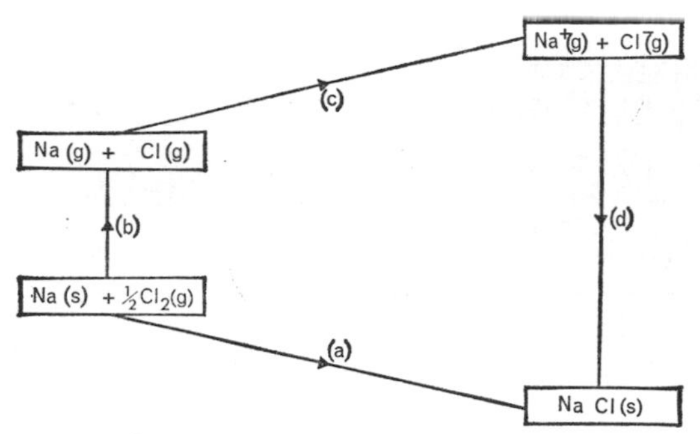

Fig. 6.1. Thermochemical (Born–Haber) cycle for NaCl

molecules in solution which then dissociate to Na^+ and Cl^- ions, or the solid crystal is itself composed of Na^+ and Cl^- ions. Let us examine the consequences of the second alternative by first considering the thermochemical cycle illustrated in figure 6.1. In this cycle the formation of NaCl(s) from Na(s) and $\frac{1}{2}Cl_2(g)$ by two routes is formulated. Route (*a*) represents the direct formation, and the enthalpy change will be the standard enthalpy of formation of NaCl(s). Route (*b*)–(*c*)–(*d*) achieves the same end, so that the net enthalpy changes for these two routes must be identical. The enthalpy changes in kcal at 0°K and 298°K for all the processes in figure 6.1 are given in table 6.1. From reaction (7) the lattice energy of sodium chloride is defined as the decrease in enthalpy which accompanies the formation of one mole of the solid crystal from the gaseous ions. For sodium chloride it has a value of 185·09 kcal at 0°K and 185·94 kcal at 298°K. Given the necessary data, similar calculations may be performed for other solid compounds. The difference between the values at 0°K and 298°K is very small, and in practice we may use the more conveniently available data at 298°K.

TABLE 6.1: ENTHALPY CHANGES IN BORN–HABER CYCLE FOR NaCl(s) AT 0°K (ΔH°_0) AND AT 298°K (ΔH°_{298})

Reaction	ΔH°_0 (kcal)	ΔH°_{298} (kcal)	
$Na(s) + \frac{1}{2}Cl_2(g) \rightleftharpoons NaCl(s)$	−97·76	−98·23	(1)
$Na(s) \rightleftharpoons Na(g)$	26·05	25·98	(2)
$Na(g) \rightleftharpoons Na^+(g) + e$	118·48	120·03	(3)
$\frac{1}{2}Cl_2(g) \rightleftharpoons Cl(g)$	28·61	29·01	(4)
$Cl(g) + e \rightleftharpoons Cl^-(g)$	−85·81	−87·31	(5)
Addition of (2), (3), (4), and (5) gives $Na(s) + \frac{1}{2}Cl_2(g) \rightleftharpoons Na^+(g) + Cl^-(g)$	$\Delta H^\circ_0 = 87{\cdot}33$; $\Delta H^\circ_{298} = 87{\cdot}71$		(6)
and subtraction of (6) from (1) gives $Na^+(g) + Cl^-(g) \rightleftharpoons NaCl(s)$	$\Delta H^\circ_0 = -185{\cdot}09$; $\Delta H^\circ_{298} = -185{\cdot}94$		(7)

It may well be asked why we choose to discuss the energies of ionic lattices in terms of equation (7) and not in terms of equation (1). One answer is that by doing so the problem of setting up a model from which it might be possible to calculate theoretically the lattice energy to be compared with the experimental result is greatly simplified. The simplest model for the NaCl lattice is to consider the crystal to be made up of positive and negative ions in which the charge on the ion is spherically symmetrical with the force between the ions dependent only on the distance between them and independent of the direction. The structure of NaCl, which can be determined by X-ray methods, shows that each Na^+ ion has 6 nearest Cl^- neighbours at a distance r, 12 Na^+ ions at a distance $r\sqrt{2}$, a further 8 Cl^- ions at a distance $r\sqrt{3}$, 6 more Na^+ ions at a distance $r\sqrt{4}$ and so on. The Coulomb energy of a single ion in the field of one other ion of opposite charge at a distance r is given by

$$E_c = -\frac{z_1 z_2 e^2}{r} \quad (8)$$

where z_1 and z_2 are the numbers of charges on each ion and e is the electronic charge. For the chosen Na^+ in the field of all other ions in the NaCl lattice, the Coulomb energy will be

$$E_c = -\frac{z_1 z_2 e^2}{r}\left(\frac{6}{\sqrt{1}} - \frac{12}{\sqrt{2}} + \frac{8}{\sqrt{3}} - \frac{6}{\sqrt{4}} + \frac{24}{\sqrt{5}} \cdots\right) \quad (9)$$

The coefficient of $z_1 z_2(e^2/r)$ is a pure number and will depend on the particular arrangement of ions in the crystal lattice. It is called the 'Madelung constant' M and for the NaCl structure has the value 1·747558. The alternating negative and positive signs in (9) refer, respectively, to attractions between ions of opposite sign and repulsions between those of like sign.

To prevent the lattice collapsing, it is assumed that there are repulsive forces which increase sharply at small values of r. One possible form of this repulsive energy term is

$$E_{rep} = \frac{B}{r^n} \quad (10)$$

where B and n are constants. The energy U evolved per mole of compound when gaseous ions of opposite charge are brought from infinity into a solid lattice with an interionic distance r is

$$U = \frac{NMz_1 z_2 e^2}{r} - \frac{NB}{r^n} \quad (11)$$

where N is the Avogadro number. The lattice energy per mole U_0, defined as the decrease in enthalpy at 0°K when the gaseous ions from infinity are brought to their equilibrium positions in the lattice with an interionic distance r_0, will be given by (11) when the condition

$$\left(\frac{\partial U}{\partial r}\right)_{r=r_0} = 0 \quad (12)$$

is satisfied. By combining (11) and (12) we obtain the equation

$$U_0 = \frac{NMz_1 z_2 e^2}{r_0}\left(1 - \frac{1}{n}\right) \quad (13)$$

If n and r_0 can be determined independently, U_0 may be calculated from (13) and compared with ΔH_0^0 obtained thermochemically from equation (7).

The model used in this illustration was first proposed by Born in 1918. Since then there have been a number of refinements aimed either at improving the repulsive energy term, or including secondary electrical or other effects. If for a whole range of solids the theoretical values of the lattice energies from equation (13), or some refinement of it, are in satisfactory agreement with the results obtained thermochemically from equation (7), we shall have established a possible, though not necessarily unique, description of the nature of chemical bonding in such compounds. Furthermore, if the model adequately describes some solids, but does not do so satisfactorily for others, it is to be presumed that for the latter there are important departures in the nature of the bonding from that described by the ionic model. This example has been treated in some detail because it illustrates the interplay of experimental energy changes and the development of models to explain the nature of chemical bonding.

Ionization Energy and Electron Affinity

In table 6.1 two of the largest energy terms are those associated with equations (3) and (5). Equation (3) defines the first ionization energy for sodium and we may define the second ionization energy in terms of the equation

$$Na^{+}(g) \rightleftharpoons Na^{2+}(g) + e \qquad (14)$$

the third by

$$Na^{2+}(g) \rightleftharpoons Na^{3+}(g) + e \qquad (15)$$

and so on. The ionization energies should, strictly speaking, be referred to 0°K, but the difference in the corresponding values at 0°K and 298°K is comparatively insignificant. The first ionization energies of the elements are shown graphically in figure 6.2. A comparison of figure 6.2 with the free energy spectra in chapter 5 reveals a close similarity in pattern which becomes progressively less marked in the series: fluoride–chloride–bromide, oxide–sulphide, fluoride–oxide–nitride. The data shown in figure 6.2 are first ionization energies, whereas many of the positive elements exhibit oxidation states higher than one. This aspect is illustrated in table 6.2 in which the ionization energies for the elements H to Na are listed. Some of the values, especially for the higher energies, are estimates only. The stepped line in table 6.2 inserted where there is an abnormally large increase in the successive ionization energies defines

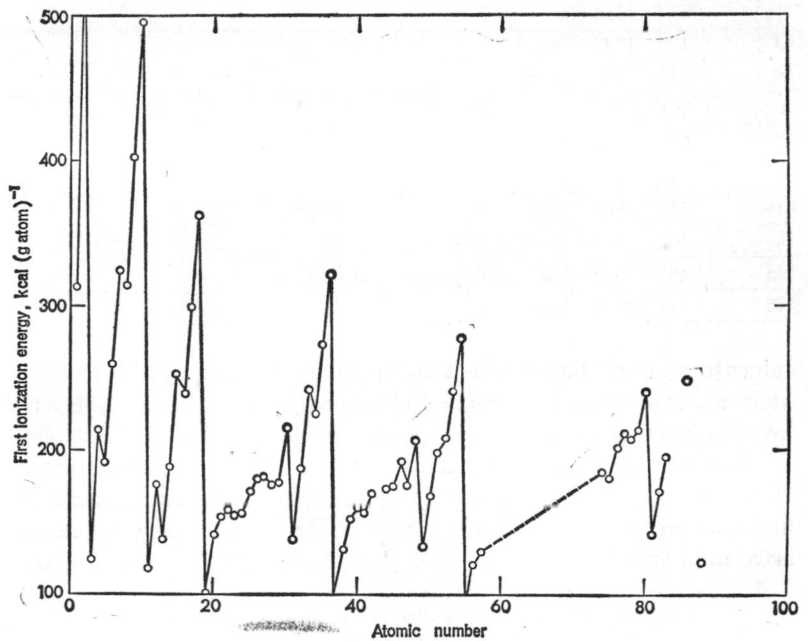

Fig. 6.2. First ionization energies of the elements

the maximum oxidation state of these elements, but this does not imply that all will participate as positive ions in this oxidation state in ionic compounds similar to NaCl. Indeed, after Be in table 6.2 few of the elements from B to F will form simple binary compounds that are solids at room temperature.

Before considering this further, it is necessary to look at the other major energy component in the Born–Haber cycle, namely equation (5) in table 6.1, which defines the electron affinity. Reliable experimental

TABLE 6.2: SUCCESSIVE IONIZATION ENERGIES OF THE ELEMENTS, H–Na (kcal(g atom)$^{-1}$)

Element	1st	2nd	3rd	4th	5th	6th	7th	8th	9th	10th
H	313									
He	567	1254								
Li	124	1743	2822							
Be	215	420	3547							
B	191	579	874	5978	7843					
C	260	562	1103	1486	9037	11240				
N	325	683	1097	1787	2256	11660				
O	314	809	1271	1781	2624	3170	16960	20000		
F	402	806	1444	2009	2633	3606	4244	21880	25300	
Ne	497	947	1480	2240	2910	3180	—	—	—	31300
Na	118	1090	1660	2280	3200	3970	4800	60900		

values for most of the elements are difficult to determine, and it has been necessary in some cases to obtain them from the Born–Haber cycle itself by assuming that the lattice energies for the lower alkali halides calculated from the model outlined in the last section (or some improvement of it) are correct. For this and other reasons, values quoted in the literature are often somewhat disparate; a few representative values are listed in table 6.3. For our present purposes it is sufficient to note that

TABLE 6.3: ELECTRON AFFINITIES OF THE HALOGENS

Equation	$-\Delta H^{0}_{298}$ kcal (g ion)$^{-1}$
$F(g) + e \rightleftharpoons F^{-}(g)$	97·8
$Cl(g) + e \rightleftharpoons Cl^{-}(g)$	87·3
$Br(g) + e \rightleftharpoons Br^{-}(g)$	82·0
$I(g) + e \rightleftharpoons I^{-}(g)$	75·7

the electron affinity displays comparatively little variation from halogen to halogen.

The test of whether a given solid compound is likely to have an ionic lattice ultimately rests on comparing the lattice energy determined thermochemically with that calculated from equation (13) or similar equation appropriate to a more refined model. Generally speaking, low values of ΔH^0 for equation (3) and negative (or small positive) values for ΔH^0 in equation (5) favour the formation of an ionic lattice. However, unfavourable values of the ionization energy and electron affinity for ions carrying multiple charges may be offset in whole or part by the term $z_1 z_2$ in the lattice energy calculated from equation (13). We may also note that equation (13) includes the Madelung constant, a dimensionless quantity related to the geometry of the lattice, which, in turn, may depend on the relative sizes of the ions. Short of doing the test calculation, it is not, therefore, an easy matter to balance these several factors mentally and correctly predict whether the particular compound will be ionic.

Problem 6.1

From the following data

$$Li(s) + \tfrac{1}{2}F_2(g) \rightleftharpoons LiF(s) \qquad \Delta H^0_{298} = -146{\cdot}3\,\text{kcal}$$
$$Li(s) \rightleftharpoons Li^+(g) + e \qquad \Delta H^0_{298} = 162{\cdot}9\,\text{kcal}$$
$$\tfrac{1}{2}F_2(g) + e \rightleftharpoons F^-(g) \qquad \Delta H^0_{298} = -79{\cdot}5\,\text{kcal}$$

(*a*) Calculate the lattice energy of lithium fluoride.

By making use of the data in tables 6.2 and 6.3 and that given above calculate:

(*b*) The heat of vaporization of Li(s) at 298°K.
(*c*) The heat of dissociation of $F_2(g)$ at 298°K.

Covalent Bonds in Diatomic Molecules

If the bond between two atoms cannot be described by the ionic model, we shall need to consider an alternative model which we call the *covalent bond.* The ionic model implied the transfer of electrons, thereby forming positive and negative ions which were held together by the electrostatic forces previously described. In covalent bonds we think of the electrons constituting the bond being shared by the two atoms involved. If the two atoms are identical, as in the chlorine molecule Cl_2 or the hydrogen molecule H_2, there is little difficulty in conceiving the sharing to be mutual, that is the electron density in the bond is symmetrical about the mid-point. These bonds we shall refer to as *normal covalent bonds*. But in a molecule H—Cl where the constituent atoms are different, it is conceivable that the bonding electrons will not be equally shared. Our first task is to examine how this problem may be approached in terms of energy.

We begin by defining the bond dissociation energy $D(\text{A—B})$ of a bond A—B in the diatomic molecule AB as the change in energy at 0°K for the reaction

$$\text{AB} \rightleftharpoons \text{A} + \text{B} \tag{16}$$

where the reactant and products are each in the ideal gas state. The bond dissociation energy measured at 298°K does not differ greatly from that at 0°K, and it is often sufficiently precise to use the standard enthalpy change ΔH^0_{298} for (16) as a measure of the bond dissociation energy. For simple diatomic molecules which are gases at room temperature, e.g. H_2, O_2, Cl_2, etc., we have corresponding to (16)

$$\text{A}_2(\text{g}) \rightleftharpoons 2\text{A}(\text{g}) \tag{17}$$

and

$$D(\text{A—A}) = 2\Delta H^0_f(\text{A(g)}) \tag{18}$$

where ΔH^0_f is simply the standard enthalpy of formation of A(g) from the molecule $A_2(g)$. By definition the standard enthalpy of formation of $A_2(g)$ is zero.

From the reaction

$$\text{HCl(g)} \rightleftharpoons \text{H(g)} + \text{Cl(g)} \tag{19}$$

$$D(\text{H—Cl}) = \Delta H^0_f(\text{H(g)}) + \Delta H^0_f(\text{Cl(g)}) - \Delta H^0_f(\text{HCl(g)}) \tag{20}$$

where the third term is the standard enthalpy of formation of HCl(g). Values for the terms on the right-hand sides of equations (18) and (20) are available, so that the bond dissociation energies for the halogens and hydrogen halides may readily be calculated. The results are given in table 6.4. In this table values have also been tabulated for the arithmetic mean of the bond dissociation energies for hydrogen (H—H) and the halide (X—X), namely $\frac{1}{2}\{D(\text{H—H}) + D(\text{X—X})\}$, and the difference Δ between this mean and the actual value of $D(\text{H—X})$. If Δ had been zero, we would have established that the dissociation energies of normal covalent bonds were additive. In these terms the value of Δ other than

TABLE 6.4: BOND DISSOCIATION ENERGIES FOR HYDROGEN, THE HALOGENS, AND HYDROGEN HALIDES

	H—H	F—F	Cl—Cl	Br—Br	I—I
Bond dissociation energy (kcal)	103·2	36	57·1	45·5	35·6
		H—F	H—Cl	H—Br	H—I
Bond dissociation energy (kcal)		134	102·2	86·3	70·5
$\frac{1}{2}\{D(\text{H—H})+D(\text{X—X})\}$		69·6	80·1	74·3	69·4
$\Delta=D(\text{H—X})-\frac{1}{2}\{D(\text{H—H})+D(\text{X—X})\}$		64.4	22·1	12·0	1·1

zero should be functionally related to the differing capacities of the two atoms H and X to attract the bonding electrons, i.e. to the difference in electronegativities of the H and X-atoms.

The ionization energy discussed in the last section may be thought of as the average of the electron attraction by an atom and its positive ion, and the electron affinity as the average of the electron attraction by an atom and its negative ion. Mullikan in 1934 suggested that the arithmetic mean of the first ionization energy and the electron affinity of an atom should give a measure of its electronegativity. The relationship between Δ and the electronegativity difference defined in these terms in explored in table 6.5. If $A_X - A_H$ is plotted against $\Delta^{\frac{1}{2}}$ an acceptable straight line, having regard to the uncertainties in the value of E, is obtained.

TABLE 6.5: CORRELATION OF Δ WITH THE ELECTRONEGATIVITY DIFFERENCE OF THE BONDED ATOMS

Element	Ionization energy I kcal	Electron affinity E kcal	$\frac{I+E}{2}$ A	Bond	$A_X - A_H$	Δ	$\Delta^{\frac{1}{2}}$
F	402	83·0	242·5	H—F	77·9	64·4	8·03
Cl	299	87·5	193·7	H—Cl	39·1	22·1	4·70
Br	273	80·6	176·8	H—Br	12·2	12·0	3·47
I	241	73·7	157·3	H—I	−7·3	1·1	1·05
H	313	16·2	164·6				

The main conclusion from this exercise is that, in the covalent bond between H and a halogen atom, the bonding electrons are not shared equally, this effect decreasing in the order F, Cl, Br, I. In comparison with the normal covalent bond, these bonds may be thought of as being partially ionic in character, the extent of this character being measured by the quantity $\Delta^{\frac{1}{2}}$, and interpreted in terms of the difference in electronegativity of the bonding atoms. Here, then, is a further illustration of the use of energy changes as a framework of reference against which the consequences of bonding models may usefully be examined.

Problem 6.2

From the following data at 298°K

$$\tfrac{1}{2}Br_2(l) \rightleftharpoons Br(g) \qquad \Delta H^0 = 26{\cdot}7\,kcal$$
$$\tfrac{1}{2}H_2(g) \rightleftharpoons H(g) \qquad \Delta H^0 = 52{\cdot}1\,kcal$$
$$\tfrac{1}{2}H_2(g) + \tfrac{1}{2}Br_2(l) \rightleftharpoons HBr(g) \qquad \Delta H^0 = -8{\cdot}7\,kcal$$
$$\tfrac{1}{2}I_2(s) \rightleftharpoons I(g) \qquad \Delta H^0 = 25{\cdot}5\,kcal$$

$D(H—I) = 70{\cdot}5\,kcal$; heat of vaporization of $Br_2(l) = 7{\cdot}4\,kcal\,mole^{-1}$; heat of sublimation of $I_2(s) = 14{\cdot}9\,kcal\,mole^{-1}$.

(*a*) Calculate the bond dissociation energies of Br—Br, I—I, and H—Br and compare your results with the corresponding values in table 6.4.
(*b*) Calculate the standard enthalpy of formation of HI from $H_2(g)$ and $I_2(s)$.

Covalent Bonds in Polyatomic Molecules

In this section we shall be concerned with simple polyatomic molecules of C, H, and O because for such molecules it is possible to measure with a fairly high degree of precision the heat of combustion. For such compounds this is defined in terms of an equation of the type

$$C_xH_yO_z + (x + \tfrac{1}{4}y - \tfrac{1}{2}z)O_2(g) \rightleftharpoons xCO_2(g) + \tfrac{1}{2}yH_2O(l) \qquad (21)$$

Such reactions are usually exothermic and the heat of combustion is simply $-\Delta H^0_{298}$. The states of CO_2 and H_2O are conventionally gas and liquid, respectively, and it is essential to define the state of $C_xH_yO_z$ as a solid, liquid, or gas.

There is no restriction in principle in writing down heats of combustion of organic compounds containing other elements such as N, Cl, S, but in such cases it is not always an easy matter experimentally to ensure that the whole of the N, Cl, S, etc., will be converted to appropriate single products.

For equation (21) at 298°K the standard enthalpy change ΔH^0 is given by

$$\Delta H^0 = x\Delta H_f^0(CO_2(g)) + \tfrac{1}{2}y\Delta H_f^0(H_2O(l)) - \Delta H_f^0(C_xH_yO_z) \qquad (22)$$

where $\Delta H_f^0(CO_2(g))$, $\Delta H_f^0(H_2O(l))$, and $\Delta H_f^0(C_xH_yO_z)$ are the standard enthalpies of formation of $CO_2(g)$, $H_2O(l)$, and $C_xH_yO_z$. Since the first two of these terms are known with considerable precision and $-\Delta H^0$ is the measured heat of combustion, we may determine ΔH_f^0 for the organic compound. For $H_2O(l)$ and $CO_2(g)$ we have

$$H_2(g) + \tfrac{1}{2}O_2(g) \rightleftharpoons H_2O(l)$$

$$\Delta H^0_{298\cdot16°K} = -68{,}317\cdot4 \pm 9\cdot6 \text{ cal mole}^{-1} \qquad (23)$$

$$C \text{ (graphite)} + O_2(g) \rightleftharpoons CO_2(g)$$

$$\Delta H^0_{298\cdot16°K} = -94{,}051\cdot8 \pm 10\cdot8 \text{ cal mole}^{-1} \qquad (24)$$

We illustrate this method by determining the standard enthalpy of formation for methane and benzoic acid. For methane

$$CH_4(g) + 2O_2(g) \rightleftharpoons CO_2(g) + 2H_2O(l) \qquad \Delta H^0_{298} = -210\cdot8 \text{ kcal} \qquad (25)$$

$$\Delta H^0_{298} = \Delta H_f^0(CO_2(g)) + 2\Delta H_f^0(H_2O(l)) - \Delta H_f^0(CH_4(g)) - 2\Delta H_f^0(O_2(g))$$

$$\Delta H_f^0(CH_4(g)) = -\Delta H^0_{298} + \Delta H_f^0(CO_2(g)) + 2\Delta H_f^0(H_2O(l)) - 2\Delta H_f^0(O_2(g))$$

$$= +210\cdot80 - 94\cdot05 - 2 \times 68\cdot32 - 0$$

$$= -19\cdot89 \text{ kcal}$$

For benzoic acid

$$C_6H_5COOH(s) + 7\tfrac{1}{2}O_2(g) \rightleftharpoons 7CO_2(g) + 3H_2O(l)$$

$$\Delta H^0_{298} = -771\cdot2 \text{ kcal} \qquad (26)$$

$$\Delta H^0_{298} = 7\Delta H_f^0(CO_2(g)) + 3\Delta H_f^0(H_2O(l)) - \Delta H_f^0(C_6H_5COOH(s)) - 7\tfrac{1}{2}\Delta H_f^0(O_2(g))$$

$$\Delta H_f^0(C_6H_5COOH(s)) = -\Delta H^0_{298} + 7\Delta H_f^0(CO_2(g)) + 3\Delta H_f^0(H_2O(l)) - 7\tfrac{1}{2}\Delta H_f^0(O_2(g))$$

$$= 771\cdot2 - 7 \times 94\cdot05 - 3 \times 68\cdot32 - 0$$

$$= -92\cdot1 \text{ kcal}$$

There are now available extensive tabulations of heats of combustion of organic compounds from which the standard enthalpies of formation at 298°K are readily obtainable. A few examples of heats of combustion are given in table 6.6.

TABLE 6.6: HEATS OF COMBUSTION AT 298°K OF SELECTED ORGANIC COMPOUNDS

Compound	Formula	State	Heat of combustion kcal $mole^{-1}$
methane	CH_4	g	210·8
ethane	C_2H_6	g	368·4
propane	C_3H_8	g	526·3
n-hexane	C_6H_{14}	l	989·8
cyclohexane	C_6H_{12}	l	937·8
ethylene	C_2H_4	g	331·6
acetylene	C_2H_2	g	312·0
methanol	CH_3OH	l	170·9
ethanol	C_2H_5OH	l	327·6
formaldehyde	$HCHO$	g	134·1
acetaldehyde	CH_3CHO	l	279·0
acetone	$(CH_3)_2CO$	l	426·8
diethyl ketone	$(C_2H_5)_2CO$	l	735·6
diethyl ether	$(C_2H_5)_2O$	l	651·7
formic acid	$HCOOH$	l	62·8
acetic acid	CH_3COOH	l	209·4
benzene	C_6H_6	l	782·3
toluene	$C_6H_5CH_3$	l	934·2
benzaldehyde	C_6H_5CHO	l	841·3
benzoic acid	C_6H_5COOH	s	771·2
phenol	C_6H_5OH	s	732·2
naphthalene	$C_{10}H_8$	s	1232·5

Problem 6.3

From the data in table 6.6 calculate the standard enthalpies of formation at 298°K for the compounds in the following series:

(*a*) Methane, methanol, acetaldehyde, acetic acid.

(*b*) Benzene, phenol, benzaldehyde, benzoic acid.

(*c*) What conclusions can you draw by comparing the results for these two series?

The question which we wish to pose is how this quantitative information may be used to express the strength of a chemical bond. Consider first the dissociation of the alkane $C_nH_m(g)$ at 298°K in the form

$$C_nH_m(g) \rightleftharpoons nC(g) + mH(g) \tag{27}$$

for which the reactant and the atomic products are each in the ideal gas state at this temperature. For this reaction written in reverse

$$nC(g) + mH(g) \rightleftharpoons C_nH_m(g) \tag{27a}$$

the enthalpy change is given by ΔH_f^a, where the superscript a and subscript f refer to the formation of the compound from the gaseous atoms.

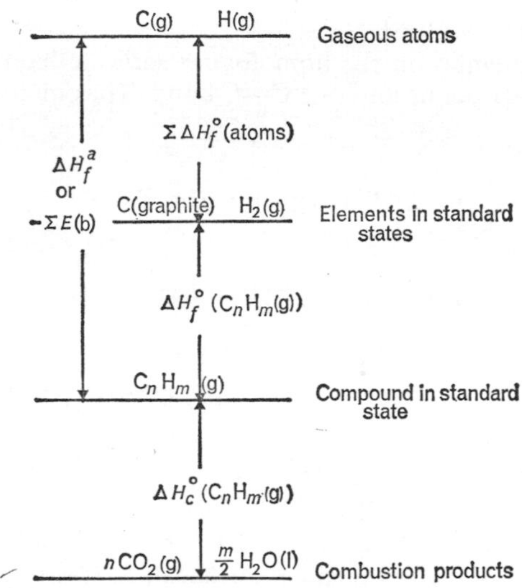

Fig. 6.3. Enthalpies of formation, combustion, atomization in relation to bond energies

It follows that for (27) the enthalpy change is $-\Delta H_f^a$ and this is given by

$$-\Delta H_f^a = n\Delta H_f^0(C(g)) + m\Delta H_f^0(H(g)) - \Delta H_f^0(C_nH_m(g)) \tag{28}$$

where the three ΔH_f^0-terms on the right-hand side refer, in order, to the standard enthalpies of formation for C(g), H(g), and $C_nH_m(g)$ from C(graphite) and $H_2(g)$. The situation is shown graphically in figure 6.3.

We now define the *sum of the bond energies* in the $C_nH_m(g)$ molecule, expressed $\sum E(b)$, by the equality

$$-\Delta H_f^a = \sum E(b) \tag{29}$$

If the C_nH_m molecule in question were methane CH_4 which we suppose to contain four C—H bonds and we arbitrarily assigned to each an equal energy, E(C—H), it follows from (28) and (29) that

$$4E(\text{C—H}) = \Delta H_f^0(\text{C(g)}) + 4\Delta H_f^0(\text{H(g)}) - \Delta H_f^0(\text{CH}_4\text{(g)}) \tag{30}$$

and provided the three quantities on the right-hand side were known, E(C—H) could be obtained.

For the next member in the homologous series, ethane CH_3—CH_3, there are six C—H bonds and one C—C bond. The equation analogous to (30) will be

$$6E(\text{C—H}) + E(\text{C—C}) = 2\Delta H_f^0(\text{C(g)}) + 6\Delta H_f^0(\text{H(g)}) - \Delta H_f^0(\text{C}_2\text{H}_6\text{(g)}) \tag{31}$$

and for the next member, propane CH_3—CH_2—CH_3

$$8E(\text{C—H}) + 2E(\text{C—C}) = 3\Delta H_f^0(\text{C(g)}) + 8\Delta H_f^0(\text{H(g)}) - \Delta H_f^0(\text{C}_3\text{H}_8\text{(g)}) \tag{32}$$

and so on. Provided the quantities on the right-hand sides of these equations are known, we may solve the equations in pairs to obtain values for the two unknowns, E(C—H) and E(C—C). If for this purpose the value for ΔH_f^0(C(g)) is taken as 170·9 kcal, ΔH_f^0(H(g)) as 52·09 kcal, and the well-established standard enthalpy of formation for the appropriate alkane for the final term, the results obtained for E(C—H) and E(C—C) are shown in table 6.7. In setting down equations (30), (31), (32), etc., and in solving them in pairs the assumption has been made that the bond energy of a particular type of bond is constant from one molecule to the next in the series. The results in table 6.7 clearly show that for the lower members at least, this assumption is not justified to a high degree of accuracy.

TABLE 6.7: BOND ENERGIES FOR E(C—H) AND E(C—C) IN ALKANES AT 298°K
(ΔH_f^0(C(g)) = 170·9 kcal; ΔH_f^0(H(g)) = 52·09 kcal)

Alkane or alkane pair	E(C—H) kcal	E(C—C) kcal
CH_4	99·29	—
CH_4/C_2H_6	99·29	78·84
C_2H_6/C_3H_8	98·73	82·20
C_3H_8/C_4H_{10}	98·35	83·70
C_4H_{10}/C_5H_{12}	98·70	82·50
C_5H_{12}/C_6H_{14}	98·60	82·82
C_6H_{14}/C_7H_{16}	98·64	82·72
C_7H_{16}/C_8H_{18}	98·64	82·70
C_8H_{18}/C_9H_{20}	98·68	82·63

This dependence of bond energy on environment within the molecule may be further illustrated by reference to the C—Cl bond. For CH_3Cl(g) we have

$$E(\text{C—Cl})+3E(\text{C—H}) = \Delta H_f^0(\text{C(g)})+3\Delta H_f^0(\text{H(g)})+\Delta H_f^0(\text{Cl(g)}) - \Delta H_f^0(\text{CH}_3\text{Cl(g)}) \quad (33)$$

and for CCl_4(g)

$$4E(\text{C—Cl}) = \Delta H_f^0(\text{C(g)})+4\Delta H_f^0(\text{Cl(g)})-\Delta H_f^0(\text{CCl}_4\text{(g)}) \quad (34)$$

and if we solve (30) and (33) for E(C—Cl) the value obtained is about 0·8 kcal greater than that obtained from (34). This kind of problem often arises where the molecule being examined contains more than one type of bond and where the method of calculation accumulates the deviations from constancy in the last bond energy evaluated. For this reason there are obvious advantages in evaluating bond energies as far as possible from molecules of the CX_n-type.

In the examples discussed, attention has been directed to simple, single bonds. There is, however, nothing in principle to prevent the extension of this idea to bonds of different types, e.g. C=C, C≡C, C=O, and to elements other than carbon. Provided the principle of additivity holds to a first approximation, it is possible to prepare a table of bond energies which is of considerable use in structural studies. Such a tabulation is given in table 6.8. The values in table 6.8 may differ from those given in some other books. This arises primarily from uncertainty in the value of $\Delta H_f^0(C(g))$ for which values ranging from 138 to 172 kcal have at various times been used. It is now widely accepted that the most probable value is 170·9 kcal.

TABLE 6.8: BOND ENERGIES IN POLYATOMIC MOLECULES

Bond	Energy (kcal)	Bond	Energy (kcal)
C—C	82·6	C—O	85·5
C=C	145·8	C=O (aldehydes)	176·0
C≡C	199·6	C=O (ketones)	179·0
N—N	39·0	C—H	98·7
N≡N	225·8	N—H	93·4
O—O	35·0	O—H	110·6

Provided the assumption of additivity is valid, bond energies may be used to calculate the standard enthalpy of formation of a compound by substituting in equations of the type given in (30), (31), (32), etc. To do this it is necessary first to formulate a structure so that the various types of bonds can be enumerated. If for such a proposed structure the value calculated from the bond energies differs by a substantial amount from the experimental value, it means that the proposed structure is an inadequate description of the molecule. We may illustrate this with reference to benzene, $C_6H_6(g)$, for which let us propose a single Kekule structure

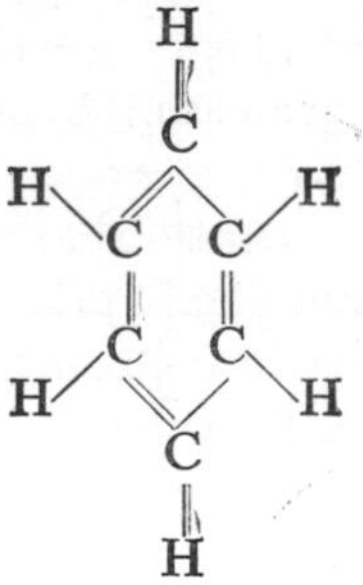

H
|
C
H ╲ ╱╲ ╱ H
C C
‖ ‖
C C
H ╱ ╲╱ ╲ H
C
|
H

for which

$$3E(\text{C—C})+3E(\text{C=C})+6E(\text{C—H}) = 6\Delta H_f^0(\text{C(g)})+6\Delta H_f^0(\text{H(g)}) - \Delta H_f^0(\text{C}_6\text{H}_6\text{(g)}) \quad (35)$$

Substitution gives

$$\Delta H_f^0(\text{C}_6\text{H}_6\text{(g)}) = 6\times170{\cdot}9+6\times52{\cdot}1-3\times82{\cdot}6-3\times145{\cdot}8-6\times98{\cdot}7$$
$$= 60{\cdot}6\,\text{kcal}$$

The experimental value for $\Delta H_f^0(C_6H_6(g))$ is, however, 19·8 kcal, clearly showing that the proposed structure is inadequate.

The difference is in the direction which points to the benzene molecule being more stable than the single proposed structure would suggest. One possible interpretation is that the structure of the benzene molecule is a resonance hybrid between the two forms

```
        H                    H
        |                    |
        C                    C
  H   //  \   H        H   /  \\   H
   \ C     C /          \ C     C /
     |     ||             ||    |
   / C     C \          / C     C \
  H   \\  /   H        H   \  //   H
        C                    C
        |                    |
        H                    H
```

and that the difference between the calculated and observed values affords a measure of the resonance energy. Examples of this kind are quite common in aromatic and other conjugated molecules.

Deviations of ΔH_f^0 for a proposed structure from the experimental value in the opposite direction to that illustrated above are usually interpreted in terms of steric strain. While a detailed discussion of this is beyond our present scope, we may note that the appropriate energy terms are again being employed as the reference framework against which the validity of particular models must ultimately be assessed.

Problem 6.4

(*a*) Formulate structures for ethane, ethylene, acetylene.
(*b*) From the data in table 6.8 calculate the enthalpies of formation of these compounds in the gaseous state at 298°K.
(*c*) Compare the results from (*b*) with values calculated from the data in table 6.6 and comment on any differences.

Problem 6.5

(*a*) Formulate structures for benzene, *n*-hexane, cyclohexane.
(*b*) From the data in table 6.8 calculate the enthalpies of formation of these compounds in the gaseous state at 298°K.
(*c*) Compare the results from (*b*) with the values calculated from the data in table 6.6 and comment on any differences.

[Heats of vaporization: benzene $= 8{\cdot}09$ kcal mole^{-1}; *n*-hexane $= 7{\cdot}54$ kcal mole^{-1}; cyclohexane $= 7{\cdot}89$ kcal mole^{-1}.]

Bond Dissociation Energies

The concept of a bond energy as used above is an abstract one. We cannot, for example, verify experimentally for a polyatomic molecule that the value listed in any tabulation for a particular bond is the correct one. What is correct and undisputed is that whatever values are attributed to individual bond energies, their sum must be equal to the enthalpy of atomization of the gaseous molecule. If we wish to examine further the energy of particular bonds we need to reintroduce the *bond dissociation energy* which, at least in principle, can be measured by special methods.

For a polyatomic molecule such as methane, the bond dissociation energy $D(CH_3\text{—}H)$ refers to the enthalpy change in the process

$$CH_4(g) \rightleftharpoons CH_3(g) + H(g) \qquad (36)$$

where CH_4, CH_3, and H are each in the ideal gas state at 0°K. In practice, it is often convenient to use the temperature of 298°K. Extending this idea, the bond dissociation energies $D(CH_2\text{—}H)$, $D(CH\text{—}H)$, and $D(C\text{—}H)$ will refer, respectively, to the reactions

$$CH_3(g) \rightleftharpoons CH_2(g) + H(g) \qquad (37)$$

$$CH_2(g) \rightleftharpoons CH(g) + H(g) \qquad (38)$$

$$CH(g) \rightleftharpoons C(g) + H(g) \qquad (39)$$

These four bond dissociation energies will, in general, be different because $D(CH_3—H)$ necessarily includes an energy component arising from the reorganization of the tetrahedral CH_4-molecule to the probably planar CH_3-radical, and there will be different reorganization terms arising in the successive dissociations. By adding equations (36) to (39) we have

$$-\Delta H_f^a(CH_4(g)) = D(CH_3—H)+D(CH_2—H)+D(CH—H) + D(C—H) \qquad (40)$$

where $\Delta H_f^a(CH_4(g))$ is the enthalpy of formation of $CH_4(g)$ from C(g) and H(g). We may also write

$$-\Delta H_f^a(CH_4(g)) = 4\bar{D}(C—H) \qquad (41)$$

where $\bar{D}(C—H)$ is called the *mean bond dissociation energy*. In this case $\bar{D}(C—H)$, but none of the component bond dissociation energies which go to form this mean, is clearly the same as the bond energy used in the last section. Where the molecule contains more than one bond type, a mean bond dissociation energy no longer has any meaning.

For diatomic molecules, e.g. H_2, Cl_2, O_2, HCl, etc., represented by AB (or AA) which are gaseous at room temperature we have by definition

$$-\Delta H_f^a = E(A—B) \qquad (42)$$

and

$$-\Delta H_f^a = D(A—B) \qquad (43)$$

so that the bond energy and the bond dissociation energy in these cases are the same. For polyatomic molecules this equality no longer holds.

7

AN ENERGETIC APPROACH TO A PROBLEM IN CATALYSIS

Heterogeneous catalysts, especially solid catalysts, are extensively used in gas reactions on an industrial scale. Their principal object is to increase the rate of the chemical reaction where only one reaction is possible, or to increase preferentially the rate of a particular reaction where more than one reaction is prone to occur. A catalyst cannot, however, alter the extent to which a reaction may proceed, i.e. the position of chemical equilibrium.

The types of catalysts that are employed are extensive and their actual number almost astronomical. Even for a single reaction many catalyst recipes differing in detail have been described to achieve some particular end consistent with other requirements, such as an adequate life or an acceptable physical form and stability. It is widely recognized that many catalysts function because of their ability to chemisorb preferentially one or more reactants, in this way to perturb the electron distribution in the adsorbed atoms or molecules, and thereby to facilitate a particular reaction—for example, metals which show strong tendencies to adsorb hydrogen are typically employed in hydrogenation and dehydrogenation reactions; metal oxides which are capable of adsorbing, or taking up in other ways, oxygen form the basis of many oxidation catalysts; the insulating oxides, e.g. Al_2O_3, which have the capacity to take up water, find extensive use in hydration and dehydration reactions.

The distinction between chemisorption involving strictly a monolayer and actual reaction in a thin layer on the surface of a catalyst is a difficult one to draw in operational circumstances, and progress in predicting potential catalysts has often been made by thinking in terms of a probable set of cyclic chemical reactions taking place between the reactants and the catalyst. In this section we examine one such case to illustrate how energy changes may be used as a criterion for choosing or modifying catalyst systems.

The Deacon process represented by the equation

$$2HCl(g)+\tfrac{1}{2}O_2(g)\rightleftharpoons H_2O(g)+Cl_2(g) \qquad (1)$$

originally employed a catalyst initially prepared as copper (II) chloride, but over the years a variety of oxides and chlorides of other metals alone or in combination has been suggested or patented. The question we pose is whether it is possible to predict which of the many possible systems are likely to be useful and which may be ignored.

It has long been supposed that the mechanism of the Deacon reaction on a $CuCl_2$ catalyst may be described by the following scheme:

$$2CuCl_2(s)\rightleftharpoons 2CuCl(s)+Cl_2(g) \qquad (2)$$

$$2CuCl(s)+\tfrac{1}{2}O_2(g)\rightleftharpoons CuO\,.\,CuCl_2(s) \qquad (3)$$

$$CuO\,.\,CuCl_2(s)+2HCl(g)\rightleftharpoons 2CuCl_2(s)+H_2O(g) \qquad (4)$$

From an energetic viewpoint it is convenient to add (2) and (3) to give

$$2CuCl_2(s)+\tfrac{1}{2}O_2(g)\rightleftharpoons CuO\,.\,CuCl_2(s)+Cl_2(g) \qquad (5)$$

and to look on the Deacon reaction as a combination of equations (5) and (4). Now the enthalpy of formation and entropy of $CuO\,.\,CuCl_2(s)$ differ by only very small amounts from the sums of these respective properties of $CuO(s)$ and $CuCl_2(s)$, so that we may, without incurring any serious energetic error, represent the proposed reaction scheme by the simplified equations:

$$CuCl_2(s)+\tfrac{1}{2}O_2(g)\rightleftharpoons CuO(s)+Cl_2(g) \qquad (6)$$

$$CuO(s)+2HCl(g)\rightleftharpoons CuCl_2(g)+H_2O(g) \qquad (7)$$

We know from experience that $CuCl_2$ is a satisfactory Deacon catalyst, but suffers from the disadvantage of having too high a volatility at the temperatures normally used, 400–460°C. If equations (6) and (7) adequately describe the functioning of the catalyst, we may first inquire what the values of ΔG^0 for these two equilibria are at temperatures of, say, 298–900°K. It may be shown that for our purposes it is sufficiently accurate to use the approximation

$$\Delta G_T^0 \approx \Delta H_{298}^0 - T\,\Delta S_{298}^0 \tag{8}$$

The results obtained are shown in table 7.1. Inspection of this table reveals that for the copper (II) system the chloride is the preferred compound, ΔG^0 for equation (7) being negative. The values of ΔG^0 for equation (6) are positive but small, and at the mean temperature of interest, say 700°K, the oxide may be formed in appreciable quantities.

TABLE 7.1: ΔG^0 VALUES FOR EQUATIONS (6) AND (7)

T°K	ΔG^0(eqn 6) kcal	ΔG^0(eqn 7) kcal
298	8·5	−17·7
500	6·1	−12·2
700	3·7	−6·7
900	1·3	−1·3

From this known case, a possible criterion for a Deacon catalyst may be formulated, namely that the standard free energy change for reactions of the type (6) and (7) shall in the temperature range of interest have small values. It is unnecessary at this stage to impose any restriction on whether the oxide or chloride shall be the energetically preferred compound.

In terms of this criterion our problem reduces to evaluating the oxide/chloride pairs of other divalent metals, and of monovalent, trivalent, and tetravalent metals. If this is done, the results for some possible systems are shown in figures 7.1–7.4. From figure 7.1 there are clearly some acceptable alternatives to copper (II); from figure 7.2 it is also clear that the monovalent metals do not meet the proposed criteria; but from figure 7.3 we conclude that there are some trivalent metals, Sc, Y, Er, and possibly Fe and Cr, which, in this decreasing order, meet the requirements; figure 7.4 suggests that the quadrivalent elements are likely to be rather less satisfactory than the trivalent metals. From these

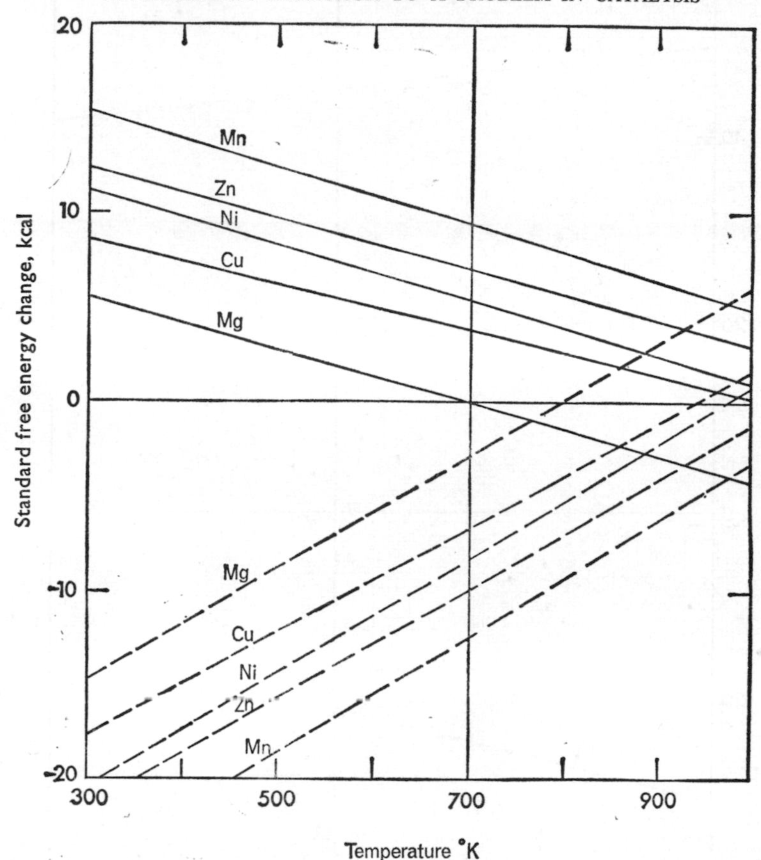

Fig. 7.1. Standard free energy changes as functions of temperature for the reactions
Full line: $XCl_2(s) + \frac{1}{2}O_2(g) \rightleftharpoons XO(s) + Cl_2(g)$
Broken line: $XO(s) + 2HCl(g) \rightleftharpoons XCl_2(s) + H_2O(g)$

considerations we may restrict ourselves to the divalent (figure 7.1) and trivalent (figure 7.3) metals.

If figure 7.1 be superimposed on figure 7.3 and we focus attention on, say, the lines for Cu and the lanthanide Er, there is defined in the centre of the diagram a diamond-shaped area, bordered on one set of opposite

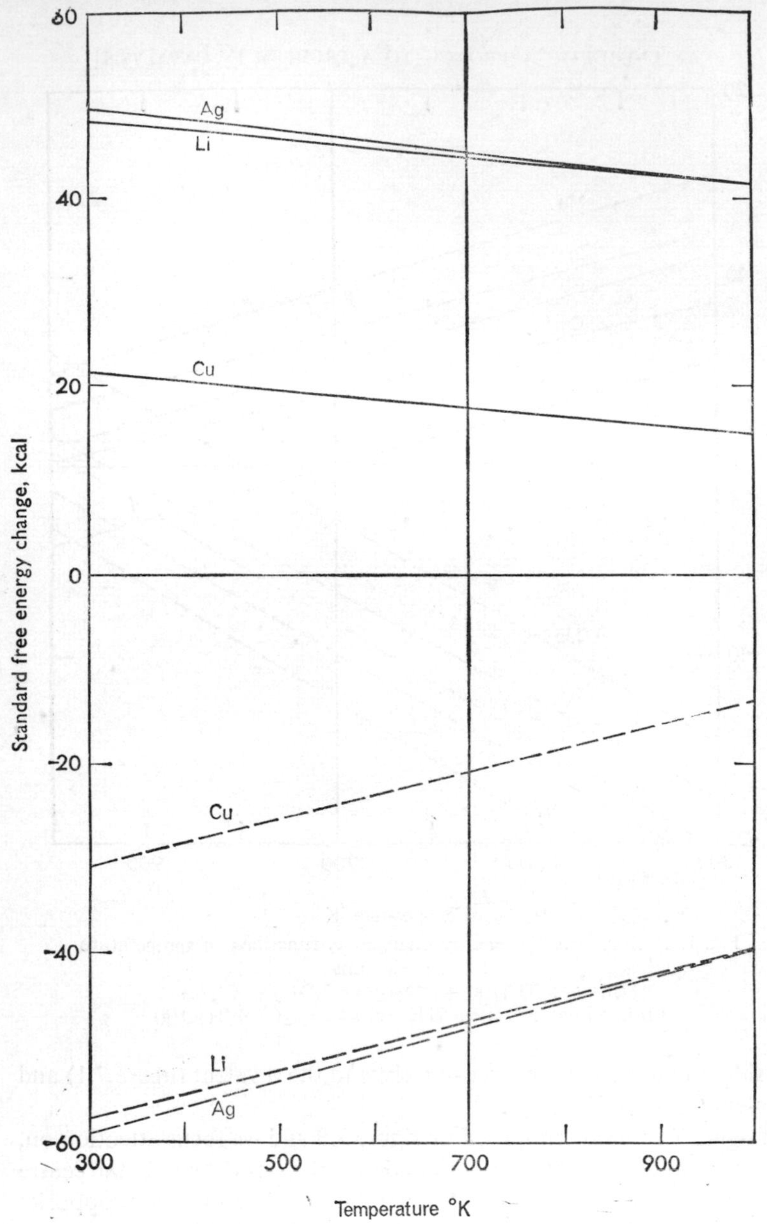

Fig. 7.2. Standard free energy changes as functions of temperature for the reactions
Full line: $2XCl(s) + \frac{1}{2}O_2(g) \rightleftharpoons X_2O(s) + Cl_2(g)$
Broken line: $X_2O(s) + 2HCl(g) \rightleftharpoons 2XCl(s) + H_2O(g)$

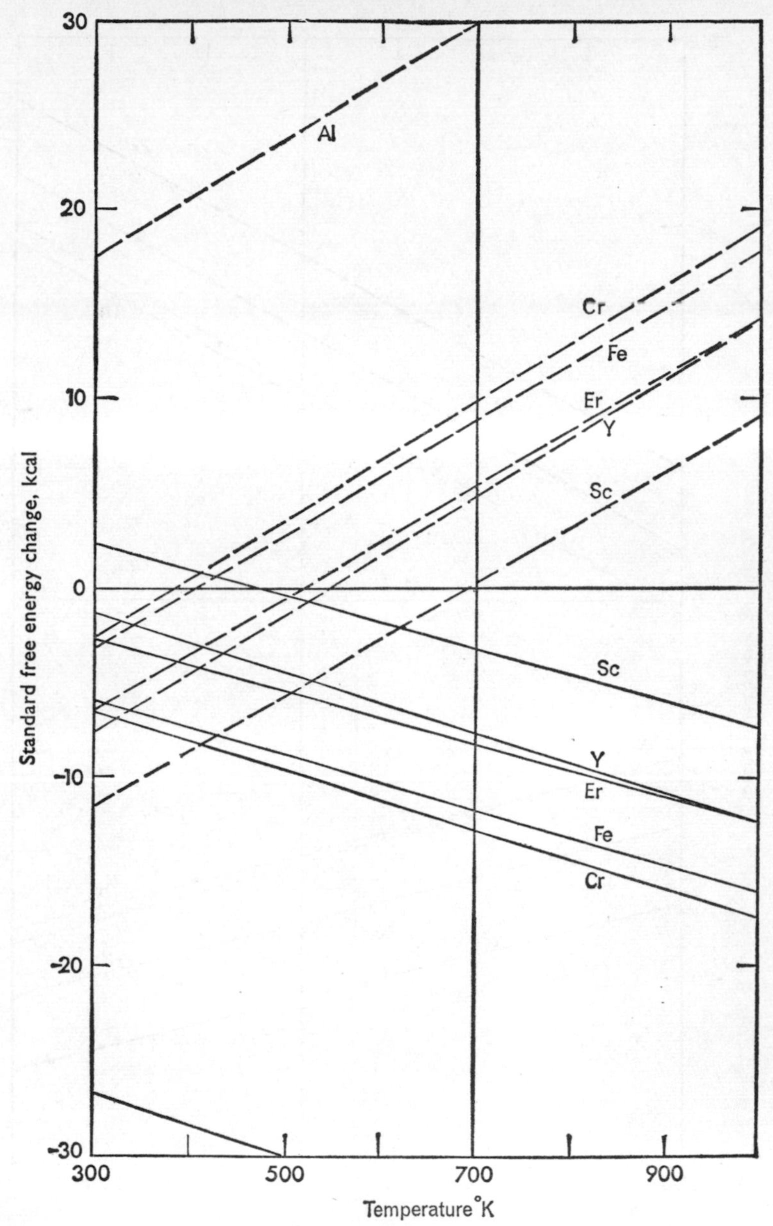

Figure 7.3. Standard free energy changes as functions of temperature for the reactions

Full line: $\frac{2}{3}XCl_3(s) + \frac{1}{2}O_2(g) \rightleftharpoons \frac{1}{3}X_2O_3(s) + Cl_2(g)$

Broken line: $\frac{1}{3}X_2O_3(s) + 2HCl(g) \rightleftharpoons \frac{2}{3}XCl_3(s) + H_2O(g)$

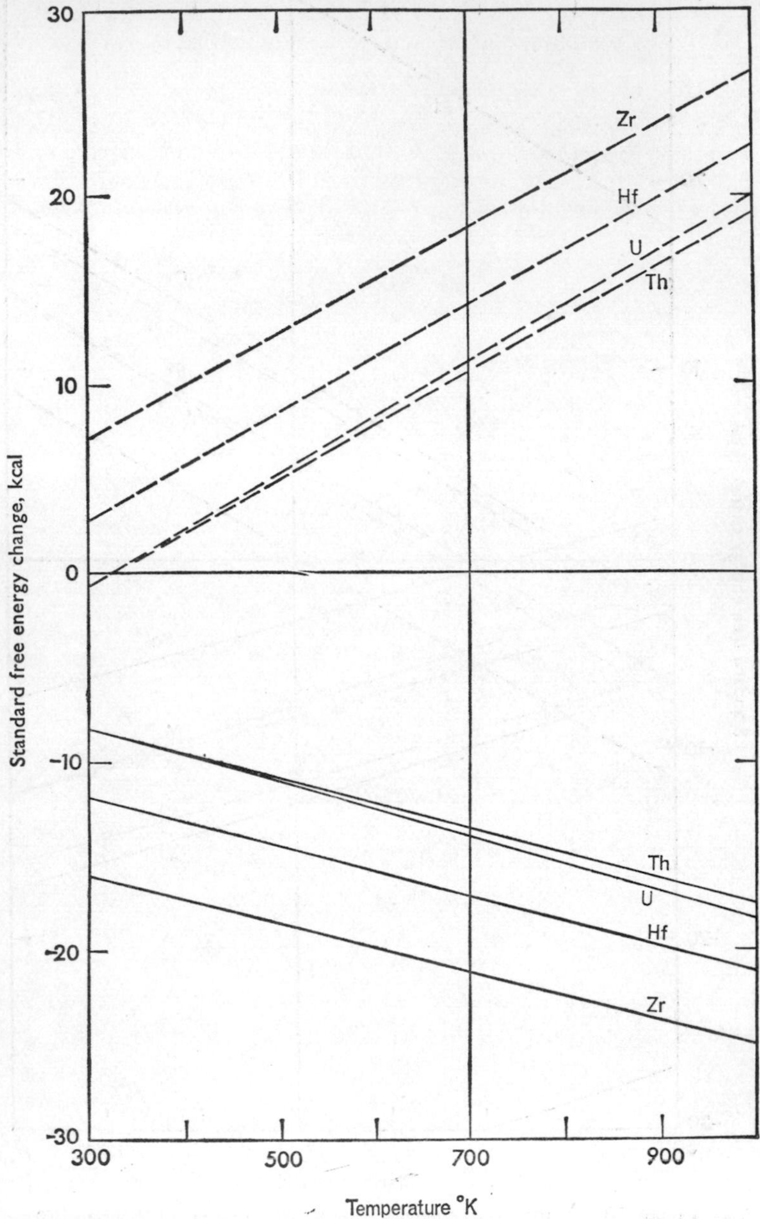

Fig. 7.4. Standard free energy changes as functions of temperature for the reactions

Full line: $\frac{1}{2}XCl_4(s) + \frac{1}{2}O_2(g) \rightleftharpoons \frac{1}{2}XO_2(s) + Cl_2(g)$

Broken line: $\frac{1}{2}XO_2(s) + 2HCl(g) \rightleftharpoons \frac{1}{2}XCl_4(s) + H_2O(g)$

sides by the free energy lines for reactions of type (6) and on the other by lines for corresponding reactions of type (7). Within such a defined area, provided always that the northern and southern intersections are at sufficiently small values of the standard free energy change, an advantageous combination of oxide and chloride of the two component metals should exist. In one pair, the oxide is the energetically favoured compound; and in the other, the chloride. Other potentially suitable combinations may similarly be selected from these graphs.

All of the many and varied claims that have been made in the patent literature for these catalysts can, in fact, be adequately explained and understood in terms of the analysis outlined above. Many claims have, for example, been made for the copper–lanthanide system to which reference has been made.

If the proposed reaction scheme is valid, the energetic analysis outlined above is capable of defining the necessary conditions for catalytic activity for the Deacon process, but is incapable by its very nature of defining the sufficient conditions. Such an analysis can yield definitive negative results, that is, it can exclude systems which are energetically unfavourable; but it tells us nothing of the rates at which the postulated reactions will proceed. If, for the sake of argument, the rate at which equation (6) proceeded was very high and that for equation (7) virtually zero, there would be no effective regeneration of the chloride even though the free energy situation were favourable. The general question of the rates of chemical reactions as distinct from the position of equilibrium will be the subject of our concluding chapter.

There is a further limitation on the energetic analysis which has been used. The data employed in calculating ΔG^0 refer to the various chemical substances in their defined bulk states. It is possible, however, that reactions of the type (6) and (7) are largely confined to thin surface layers for which the enthalpy and entropy data for defined bulk states may not be wholly applicable. In spite of these limitations, the method provides a useful guide to experimental studies and illustrates a first-level practical analysis in terms of energy of a proposed catalytic mechanism.

Problem 7.1

Ethylene oxide, C_2H_4O, is made commercially by passing a mixture of ethylene and oxygen at a total pressure of 1 atm over a silver catalyst at a temperature of about 280°C.

(*a*) By examining the reactions

$$Ag_2O(s) \rightleftharpoons 2Ag(s) + \tfrac{1}{2}O_2(g)$$
$$Ag_2O(s) + C_2H_4(g) \rightleftharpoons 2Ag(s) + C_2H_4O(g)$$

under the operating conditions, predict whether the catalyst is likely to have the composition corresponding to Ag or Ag_2O.

(*b*) What predictions, if any, may be made after examining the energy changes in these reactions?

$$C_2H_4(g) + \tfrac{1}{2}O_2(g) \rightleftharpoons C_2H_4O(g)$$
$$C_2H_4(g) + 3O_2(g) \rightleftharpoons 2CO_2(g) + 2H_2O(g)$$

(*c*) While ethylene oxide may be made in the manner outlined above, propylene oxide has not been made successfully in this way. From an energetic analysis of the relevant reactions, what conclusions may be drawn concerning this difference in behaviour of the two hydrocarbons?

The following data at 298°K are required:

Substance	ΔH_f^0 kcal mole^{-1}	S^0 cal deg^{-1} mole^{-1}	C_p^0 cal deg^{-1} mole^{-1}
Ag(s)	0	10·2	6·1
Ag_2O(s)	−7·3	29·1	15·7
O_2(g)	0	49·0	7·0
C_2H_4(g)	12·5	52·5	10·4
C_3H_6(g)	4·9	63·8	15·3
C_2H_4O(g)	−12·2	58·1	11·5
C_3H_6O(g)	−22·0	67·1	17·4
CO_2(g)	−94·1	51·1	8·9
H_2O(g)	−57·8	45·1	8·0

8

THE RATES OF CHEMICAL REACTIONS

The study of the dynamics of chemical change poses two separate questions:

(i) How far may a reaction as written proceed?
(ii) How fast will it proceed?

In the preceding chapters we have been concerned with examining how energy changes, notably free energy changes, enable progress to be made in finding an answer to the first question. Our task in this chapter is to examine briefly the second of these questions.

Nearly a century ago, it was recognized that the rate or velocity of a chemical reaction depended not on the total masses of the reacting substances, but on their concentrations. For the general reaction

$$aA + bB \rightleftharpoons cC + dD \tag{1}$$

the rate may be expressed as the rate of decrease in the concentration of A or B with time, i.e. $-d[A]/dt$ or $-d[B]/dt$, or the rate of increase in the concentration of C or D with time, i.e. $d[C]/dt$ or $d[D]/dt$. The general equation for the rate of reaction (1) may be written

$$-\frac{d[A]}{dt} \propto [A]^n[B]^m \tag{2}$$

expressing the fact that the rate is proportional to the concentration of A raised to some power n and the concentration of B to some power m. The sum $m+n$ is called the *overall order of the reaction*, and n and m the orders with respect to A and B, respectively. In some cases $n = a$ and $m = b$, but this is *not* true in general.

Equation (2) may be rewritten as

$$-\frac{d[\mathrm{A}]}{dt} = k[\mathrm{A}]^n[\mathrm{B}]^m \tag{3}$$

where k, the proportionality constant, is defined as the *specific reaction rate* and is sometimes called the *rate constant* or *velocity constant*. To determine k experimentally we may proceed broadly in one of two ways: Either we could measure $-d[\mathrm{A}]/dt$ as a function of [A] and [B] for a sufficient number of values and determine by substitution in (3) the values of n, m, and k. Alternatively, we could for particular numerical values of n and m integrate (3) with respect to time, substitute in the integrated equation experimentally determined values of [A] and [B] for various value of t, and solve for k. Provided n and m have been correctly chosen, the values of k obtained will be constant. Much of this task is done graphically in practice, and all we need note here is the definition of k in terms of (3) and how, in principle, it may be determined experimentally.

For most chemical reactions the specific reaction rate k is found experimentally to vary with temperature and if $\ln k$ is plotted against $1/T$ where T is in °K, the resulting graph is a straight line. This relationship between k and T, called the *Arrhenius equation*, may be written

$$k = A\,e^{-E/RT} \tag{4}$$

where A is called the *frequency factor* or *action constant*, E the *activation energy* and R is the *gas constant*. It follows from (4) that

$$\ln k = \ln A - \frac{E}{RT} \tag{5}$$

i.e. the slope of the graph $\ln k$ against $1/T$ will be $-(E/R)$, and the intercept $\ln A$. It has also been established experimentally that, since the slope $-(E/R)$ is either zero or negative, E is either zero or positive. Our principal task is to interpret the activation energy E and the frequency factor A.

Problem 8.1

The specific reaction rates for the decomposition of N_2O_5 at various temperatures are as follows:

Temperature, °K	298	308	318	328	338
$k \times 10^5$, sec^{-1}	1·7	6·6	24·9	75·0	240

Determine graphically the values of A and E in the Arrhenius equation.

The Activation Energy

The activation energy may be looked upon as the additional energy which the reactants need to acquire for reaction to take place. Diagrammatically, this quantity may be represented (as in figure 8.1) as an energy barrier separating the initial state (the reactants) from the final state (the products).

The abscissa in such a diagram is called the *reaction coordinate* which, while difficult to define in concrete terms, may be thought of as representing the progress of the reaction from left to right. The state at the top of the barrier is called the *transition state* in which we have not a normal molecule, but an unstable complex of high energy for which vibration in a particular mode leads to its decomposition to form products. This complex is called the *activated complex.*

In figure 8.1*a* the difference in energy between the reactants and products is simply ΔH, the enthalpy change which accompanies the reaction. It is, as may be seen from the diagram, dependent only on the initial state (the reactants) and the final state (the products) and is independent of the value of E_f. For the reverse reaction the activation energy is shown as E_b and from figure 8.1*a*

$$\Delta H = E_f - E_b \qquad (6)$$

In the example illustrated in figure 8.1*a*, ΔH is negative, i.e. the reaction from left to right is exothermic, the products having a lower total energy than the reactants. If the original reaction were endothermic as in figure 8.1*b*, ΔH would be positive, but the relationship between E_f, E_b, and ΔH in equation (6) would again hold.

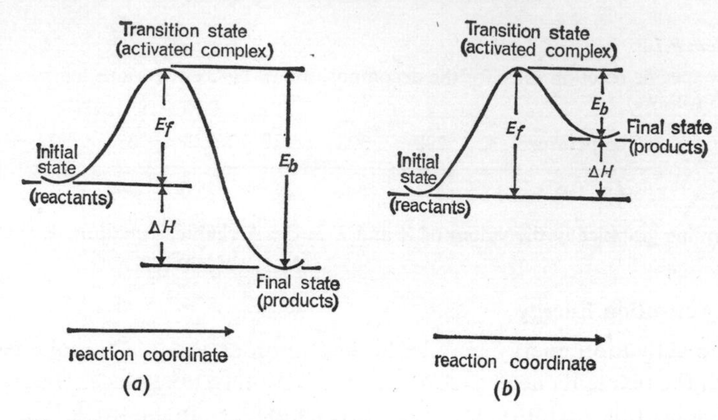

Fig. 8.1. Activation energy as an energy barrier between reactants and products: *(a)* exothermic reaction; *(b)* endothermic reaction

From equation (5) we may write for the forward and reverse reactions

$$\ln k_f = \ln A_f - \frac{E_f}{RT} \tag{7}$$

$$\ln k_b = \ln A_b - \frac{E_b}{RT} \tag{8}$$

and subtracting (8) from (7)

$$\ln \frac{k_f}{k_b} = \ln \frac{A_f}{A_b} - \frac{(E_f - E_b)}{RT} \tag{9}$$

and by substituting from (6)

$$\ln \frac{k_f}{k_b} = \ln \frac{A_f}{A_b} - \frac{\Delta H}{RT} \tag{10}$$

This may be compared with the integral of the van't Hoff equation

$$\frac{d \ln K}{dT} = \frac{\Delta H}{RT^2} \tag{11}$$

i.e.

$$\ln K = \ln C - \frac{\Delta H}{RT} \tag{12}$$

where K is the equilibrium constant and C is a constant. It follows from equations (10) and (12) therefore that

$$K = \frac{k_f}{k_b} \tag{13}$$

This important conclusion illustrates the relationship between the equilibrium constant for a chemical reaction and the specific reaction rates of the forward and reverse reactions which are the two opposing dynamic processes constituting the equilibrium.

In the Arrhenius equation we noted that the activation energy and the temperature occur in the term $e^{-E/RT}$, implying that the frequency factor is independent of temperature. It has often been claimed that a rise of 10°C doubles the speed of a chemical reaction. If this were true

$$\frac{k_2}{k_1} = \frac{2}{1} = \frac{A\,e^{-E/RT_2}}{A\,e^{-E/RT_1}} = \exp\left[-\frac{E}{R}\left(\frac{1}{T_2} - \frac{1}{T_1}\right)\right] \tag{14}$$

where the suffix 2 refers to the higher and the suffix 1 to the lower temperature. If T_1 were 300°K and T_2 310°K, substitution in (14) and rearrangement gives

$$E = \frac{2{\cdot}303 \times \log 2 \times 1{\cdot}99 \times 300 \times 310}{10}$$
$$= 12{\cdot}8\,\text{kcal mole}^{-1} \tag{15}$$

This statement is true for the temperature rise from 300 to 310°K only for a reaction in which E has this value, but for an interval of 10 deg at some other temperature a doubling of the rate would only occur if E had some other appropriate value. For example, for a reaction to double in rate between 1000 and 1010°K, E would need to have a value of 139 kcal mole^{-1}.

The value of E will depend vitally on the energy of the transition state. For example, let us suppose there is a reaction for which E is 35 kcal mole^{-1} and we could by some means provide a new transition state at a value of E of 30 kcal mole^{-1}. If the frequency factor A remained the same, the reaction rate according to (4) would at 500°K increase by a factor of

$$\frac{e^{-30,000/RT}}{e^{-35,000/RT}} = e^5 = 148 \cdot 41 \quad (16)$$

From this illustration it is evident that even small reductions in E can greatly increase the specific rate of a chemical reaction. This is one of the principal functions of a catalyst, namely to provide a new transition state, i.e. an alternative reaction path, of lower energy. Furthermore, if we have a reactant A which in the uncatalysed reaction proceeds at comparable rates in two ways represented by

$$A \begin{smallmatrix} \nearrow B \\ \searrow C \end{smallmatrix} \quad (17)$$

the introduction of a catalyst which preferentially reduces the activation energy of one of these paths will greatly enhance the rate of that particular reaction. One of the explanations for the specificity of catalysts for particular reactions is to be found in these terms.

Problem 8.2

A given substance decomposes into two products A and B by parallel paths for which the specific reaction rates k_A and k_B, respectively, are given by

$$k_A = 10^{16}e^{-35,000/RT}$$
$$k_B = 10^{14}e^{-25,000/RT}$$

Calculate the temperature at which

(*a*) The two products are formed at the same rate;
(*b*) B is formed 100 times as fast as A.

Problem 8.3

A substance decomposes by two parallel reactions for which the specific reaction rates are k_A and k_B, respectively. If at 298°K, $\frac{k_A}{k_B} = 10$ and at 328°K, $\frac{k_A}{k_B} = 0 \cdot 1$, calculate the difference in the energies of activation for the two reactions.

Problem 8.4

For the reaction

$$A(g) \underset{k_b}{\overset{k_f}{\rightleftharpoons}} B(g) + C(g)$$

the values of k_f and k_b at 298°K are $2 \times 10^{-1} \text{sec}^{-1}$ and $2 \times 10^{-4} \text{sec}^{-1}$, respectively. At 308°K the corresponding values are $4 \times 10^{-1} \text{sec}^{-1}$ and $4 \times 10^{-4} \text{sec}^{-1}$. Calculate

(*a*) the activation energies for the forward and reverse reactions;
(*b*) the enthalpy change for the reaction.

The Transition State Theory

One of the consequences of supposing in a chemical reaction that there exists a transition state at an energy E above the initial state is that the rate of the reaction may be expressed as being equal to the number of activated complexes passing over the energy barrier per unit of time. This will be given by the concentration of the activated complexes multiplied by the average velocity of passage. To simplify this calculation, it is assumed that the activated complexes are in equilibrium with the reactants. For the scheme

$$A + B \rightleftharpoons AB^{\ddagger} \rightarrow \text{products} \tag{18}$$

A and B are the reactants, $AB^{\ddagger}$ is the activated complex in equilibrium with A and B for which

$$K^{\ddagger} = \frac{[AB^{\ddagger}]}{[A][B]} \tag{19}$$

whence

$$[AB^{\ddagger}] = K^{\ddagger}[A][B] \tag{20}$$

The average velocity with which the complex moves across the barrier may be shown by statistical quantum mechanics to be kT/h where k is the Boltzmann constant ($= R/N$ where N is the Avogadro number) and h is Planck's constant. Both are universal constants. The rate of the reaction will then be given by

$$-\frac{d[A]}{dt} = \frac{kT}{h} K^{\ddagger}[A][B] \tag{21}$$

and if the rate is also given by

$$-\frac{d[A]}{dt} = k_2[A][B] \tag{22}$$

where k_2 is the specific reaction rate, it follows that

$$k_2 = \frac{kT}{h}K^{\ddagger} \tag{23}$$

But $K^{\ddagger}$, being an equilibrium constant, is related to a standard free energy change $\Delta G^{0\ddagger}$ by the equation

$$\Delta G^{0\ddagger} = -RT\ln K^{\ddagger} \tag{24}$$

and remembering that

$$\Delta G^{0\ddagger} = \Delta H^{0\ddagger} - T\,\Delta S^{0\ddagger} \tag{25}$$

substitution for $K^{\ddagger}$ gives*

$$k_2 = \frac{kT}{h}\exp\left(-\frac{\Delta G^{0\ddagger}}{RT}\right) = \frac{kT}{h}\exp\left(\frac{\Delta S^{0\ddagger}}{R}\right)\exp\left(-\frac{\Delta H^{0\ddagger}}{RT}\right) \tag{26}$$

The quantities $\Delta G^{0\ddagger}$, $\Delta H^{0\ddagger}$, and $\Delta S^{0\ddagger}$ are the free energy, enthalpy, and entropy of activation and refer to the changes in standard free energy, enthalpy, and entropy for the reaction

$$A + B \rightleftharpoons AB^{\ddagger} \tag{27}$$

If (26) is compared with the Arrhenius equation in the form

$$k_2 = A\exp\left(-\frac{E}{RT}\right) \tag{4}$$

we might by inspection seek to equate E with $\Delta H^{0\ddagger}$ and A with $(kT/h)\exp(\Delta S^{0\ddagger}/R)$. This is not quite correct as the detailed comparison of the differentials with respect to T shows, the actual equalities being

$$E = \Delta H^{0\ddagger} + RT \tag{28}$$

and

$$A = \frac{ekT}{h}\exp\left(\frac{\Delta S^{0\ddagger}}{R}\right) \tag{29}$$

* Here we use exp instead of e for the exponential function.

We have thus transformed the two empirical quantities E and A into quantities which could be evaluated if $\Delta H^{0\ddagger}$ and $\Delta S^{0\ddagger}$ for reaction (27) could be determined. If $AB^{\ddagger}$ were an ordinary molecule, it would be feasible to measure its enthalpy and entropy, and from these and the corresponding values for A and B, the quantities $\Delta H^{0\ddagger}$ and $\Delta S^{0\ddagger}$ could be calculated. The activated complex $AB^{\ddagger}$ is not, however, a normal stable molecule which could be examined experimentally in isolation.

For the present we shall have to content ourselves with evaluating $\Delta H^{0\ddagger}$ and $\Delta S^{0\ddagger}$ by means of equations (28) and (29) from the experimentally determined values of E and A. The values obtained for $\Delta S^{0\ddagger}$ are particularly instructive. Since k and h are universal constants and e is known, the value of ekT/h may be calculated at any temperature. At 300°K it is $1{\cdot}7 \times 10^{13}\ \text{sec}^{-1}$.

For a number of simple reactions in the gas phase involving the decomposition of single molecules by the breaking of a particular bond, the activated complex might be expected to be very like the reactant in its shape and organization. If this were so, $\Delta S^{0\ddagger}$ would be very close to zero, and $\exp(\Delta S^{0\ddagger}/R)$ close to unity. Reversing this argument, experimental values of A close to ekT/h would indicate that this is a nearly adequate description of the activated complex.

In reactions in which two reactant molecules come together to form the complex, the latter is likely to be more ordered than the separated reactants, two entities having organized themselves into one, and we would expect $\Delta S^{0\ddagger}$ to be negative. In a number of special cases of reactions of the type

$$A + B \rightleftharpoons AB^{\ddagger} \rightarrow AB \tag{30}$$

$\Delta S^{0\ddagger}$ is not very different from ΔS^{0} for the reaction. This means that $S^{0\ddagger}$ for the complex $AB^{\ddagger}$ does not differ appreciably from S^{0} for the product AB. Again, there are cases in which $\Delta S^{0\ddagger}$ is positive, indicating that the entropy of the complex is greater than that of the reactants, but the more usual case is for $\Delta S^{0\ddagger}$ to be negative.

One of the principal aims of this chapter was to underline the distinction between rates of chemical reactions and the extent to which reactions may proceed. In discussing the former we have in terms of the activated complex considered an equilibrium to exist between an initial and a transition state in order to provide more adequate working tools in terms of energy to describe the rates of passage to the final state.

Problem 8.5

For the decomposition of N_2O_5 in the temperature range 300–340°K the values of A and E in the Arrhenius equation are $A = 1{\cdot}5 \times 10^{13}\,\text{sec}^{-1}$, $E = 24{\cdot}4\,\text{kcal mole}^{-1}$. Calculate

(*a*) $\Delta G^{0\ddagger}$, (*b*) $\Delta H^{0\ddagger}$, (*c*) $\Delta S^{0\ddagger}$ for the reaction at 340°K.
(*d*) What conclusions can you draw from the value of $\Delta S^{0\ddagger}$ about the nature of the activated complex?

[$h = 6{\cdot}625 \times 10^{-27}\,\text{erg sec}$, $k = 1{\cdot}38 \times 10^{-16}\,\text{erg deg}^{-1}$]

Conclusion

Except for our excursion into rate processes in this chapter, we have been concerned with energy changes in chemistry—in brief, with chemical thermodynamics. Thermodynamics deals with matter in bulk, that is, with macroscopic objects. It does not try to explain why a substance has particular properties, but aims to link together observable properties of macroscopic objects in order that a knowledge of a few will permit the calculation or prediction of many others. Scientists, however, have not been content to rest at this stage, but have repeatedly sought to account for these macroscopic properties in terms of microscopic pictures of molecules and atoms, ions and electrons.

From a picture of the microscopic world built up largely from the accumulation of molecular and spectroscopic data, it has proved possible by use of statistical mechanics, a special type of mathematical language involving both mechanical and probability arguments, to determine in favourable cases what macroscopic behaviour or properties to expect. The validity of the macroscopic results obtained by statistical mechanics is much dependent on the detailed microscopic picture that is used. While the thermodynamic conclusions are independent of any microscopic representation, statistical mechanics is the bridge which enables the macroscopic properties to be interpreted in terms of microscopic models.

APPENDIX—SOURCES OF DATA

The following list of references, which is in no sense exhaustive, covers a number of conveniently available compilations of data for use in conjunction with the text.

C. D. HODGMAN, edit., *Handbook of Chemistry and Physics*, any late edition (Chemical Rubber Publishing Co., Cleveland, Ohio)

J. H. PERRY, edit., *Chemical Engineers' Handbook*, 4th edn. (McGraw–Hill, New York, 1963)

N. A. LANGE, *Handbook of Chemistry*, 10th edn. (McGraw-Hill, New York, 1961).

F. D. ROSSINI, D. D. WAGMAN, W. H. EVANS, S. LEVINE and I. JAFFE, *Selected Values of Chemical Thermodynamic Properties*, National Bureau of Standards, Circular 500 (U.S. Govt. Printing Office, Washington, D.C., 1952)

F. D. ROSSINI, K. S. PITZER, R. L. ARNOTT, R. M. BRAUN and G. C. PIMENTEL, *Selected Values of Physical & Thermodynamic Properties of Hydrocarbons and Related Compounds*, American Petroleum Institute Research Project 44 (Carnegie Press, Pittsburgh, Penn., 1953)

D. R. STULL and G. C. SINKE, *Thermodynamic Properties of the Elements*, (American Chemical Society, Washington, 1956)

O. KUBASCHEWSKI and E. L. EVANS, *Metallurgical Thermochemistry*, 3rd edn. (Pergamon, London, 1958)

G. M. AYLWARD and T. J. V. FINDLAY, editors, *Chemical Data Book*, 2nd edn. (Wiley, Sydney, Australia, 1966)

W. M. LATIMER, *Oxidation Potentials*, 2nd edn. (Prentice-Hall, New York, 1952)

ANSWERS TO PROBLEMS

1.1 (*a*) CH_3COOH 4·95 mole l^{-1}; C_2H_5OH 1·52; $CH_3COOC_2H_5$ 5·44; H_2O 5·44

(*b*) 5·15; 2·07; 4·10; 10·28

(*c*) 8·04; 0·60; 4·36; 4·36

(*d*) 3·40; 3·40; 1·98; 22·82

(*e*) The relative concentrations of the components would be unchanged.

1.2 (*a*) $K_c = \dfrac{[CH_3CH(OC_2H_5)_2][H_2O]}{[C_2H_5OH]^2[CH_3CHO]}$; (*b*) $7{\cdot}2 \times 10^{-2} (\text{mole}\, l^{-1})^{-1}$

1.3 (*a*) $K_p = \dfrac{(p_{SO_3})}{(p_{SO_2})(p_{O_2})^{\frac{1}{2}}}$; $K_c = \dfrac{[SO_3]}{[SO_2][O_2]^{\frac{1}{2}}}$

(*b*) $3{\cdot}09\,(\text{mmHg})^{-\frac{1}{2}}$; (*c*) $676\,(\text{mole}\, l^{-1})^{-\frac{1}{2}}$

(*d*) $K_p = \dfrac{(p_{SO_3})^2}{(p_{SO_2})^2(p_{O_2})}$; $K_c = \dfrac{[SO_3]^2}{[SO_2]^2[O_2]}$

(*e*) $7225\,\text{atm}^{-1}$; $4{\cdot}58 \times 10^5\,(\text{mole}\, l^{-1})^{-1}$

1.4 (*a*) 30·1%; (*b*) PCl_5 9·67 atm; PCl_3 4·16 atm; Cl_2 4·16 atm

1.5 (*a*) 2·89; (*b*) 3·75; (*c*) $p_{CO} = 0{\cdot}21$ atm; $p_{CO_2} = 0{\cdot}79$ atm

1.6 (*a*) $CuCl_2.2H_2O(s) \rightleftharpoons CuCl_2.H_2O(s) + H_2O(g)$; $K_p = p_{H_2O}$
(*b*) 0·32 atm; 0·0049 atm; (*c*) no

2.1 −552 cal

2.2 (*a*) 5×10^{-2} atm; (*b*) 17·9%

2.3 (*a*) 6·9 kcal, 10^{-5}; (*b*) −123·0, $10^{90}\,\text{atm}^{-1}$; (*c*) 21·8, 10^{-16} atm
(*d*) 14·9, 10^{-11}; (*e*) 2·1, 3×10^{-2} atm; (*f*) 22mmHg

2.4 (*a*) 319·9 kcal; (*b*) 25·9; (*c*) 56·6; (*d*) 42·4; (*e*) −39·1; (*f*) 13·6; (*g*) −63·2

2.5 (*a*) 139·1 cal deg^{-1}; (*b*) −91·9; (*c*) −0·2; (*d*) 38·4; (*e*) −38·7; (*f*) 15·3; (*g*) 8·5

2.7 (*a*) 278·5 kcal; (*b*) 53·3; (*c*) 56·7; (*d*) 31·0; (*e*) −27·6; (*f*) 9·0; (*g*) −65·7

2.8 140mmHg

3.1 (*a*) 194·7 kcal; (*b*) 108·6; (*c*) 56·8; (*d*) 7·8; (*e*) −4·3; (*f*) −0·1; (*g*) −70·8

3.2 (*a*) 13·7 kcal; (*b*) 795 cal; (*c*) 36·6 cal deg^{-1}

3.3 (*a*) −9·6 kcal; (*b*) 3·4 cal; (*c*) −28·3 cal deg^{-1}

3.4 (*a*) 193·0 kcal; (*b*) 106·7; (*c*) 57·2; (*d*) 8·2; (*e*) −6·7; (*f*) −0·8; (*g*) −77·9

3.5 $\log K_{600} = 117{\cdot}7$

4.1 (*a*) 0; (*b*) −15·7 kcal; (*c*) 3·0; (*d*) −97·3; (*e*) 0

4.2 14·6 kcal

4.3 −158 cal

4.4 (*a*) 21·3 kcal: (*b*) −38·6; (*c*) −12·4; (*d*) −35·2

4.5 0·005M

4.6 $10^{-9{\cdot}8}$

4.7 (*a*) −38·0 kcal, 10^{28}; (*b*) −46·4 kcal; (*c*) −28·3 cal deg^{-1}

6.1 (*a*) 229·7 kcal $mole^{-1}$; (*b*) 38·9 kcal $mole^{-1}$; (*c*) 36·6 kcal $mole^{-1}$

6.2 (*a*) 46·0 kcal; 36·1; 87·5 (*b*) 7·1 kcal $mole^{-1}$

6.3 (*a*) −19·9 kcal $mole^{-1}$; −59·8; −45·7; −115·3
(*b*) 13·0 kcal $mole^{-1}$; −37·1; −22·0; −92·1
(*c*) Benzene has a value apparently inconsistent with that which would have been predicted by examining the two series.

6.4 (*a*) $CH_3—CH_3$; $CH_2═CH_2$; $CH≡CH$

(*b*) −20·4 kcal; 9·6; 49·0

(*c*) −24·7 kcal; 6·9; 55·6; differences due to use of bond energies appropriate to hydrocarbon compounds in general, whereas these are early members of series.

6.5 (*a*)

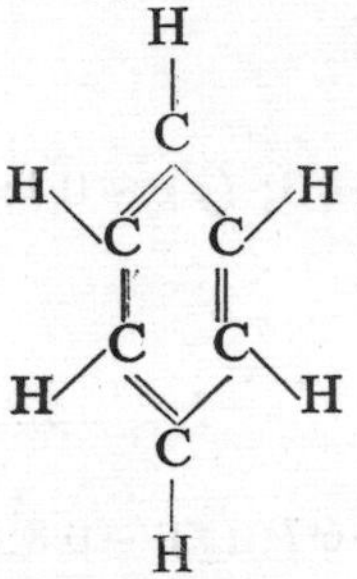

```
        H                                                        CH2
        |                                                       /   \
        C
 H    /   \\    H ; CH3—CH2—CH2—CH2—CH2—CH3;  CH2   CH2
   \C       C/                                                   |       |
    ||      ||                                                 CH2   CH2
   /C       C\                                                   \   /
 H    \\   /    H                                                CH2
        C
        |
        H
```

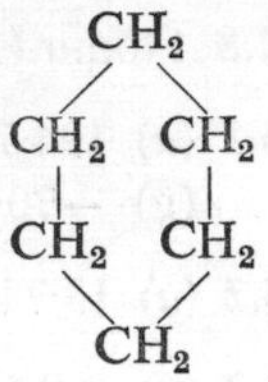

(*b*) 60·6 kcal; −40·0; −29·4

(*c*) 21·1 kcal; −45·2; −28·5; structure for benzene clearly inadequate

7.1 (*a*) silver

(*b*) Both reactions thermodynamically feasible; reaction under kinetic control.

(*c*) Reaction of propylene to propylene oxide is thermodynamically feasible. Oxidation to CO_2 is preferred reaction presumably due to kinetic factors (double bond activated by substitution of CH_3 group for H).

8.1 $10^{13·4}$; 24·8 kcal $mole^{-1}$

8.2 (*a*) 1090°K; (*b*) 545°K

8.3 29·8 kcal $mole^{-1}$

8.4 (*a*) 12·6 kcal $mole^{-1}$; 12·6; (*b*) 0 $mole^{-1}$

8.5 (*a*) 25·4 kcal; (*b*) 23·7 kcal; (*c*) −4·95 cal deg^{-1}; (*d*) the activated complex does not differ much from the N_2O_5 molecule.

LIST OF SYMBOLS

A	frequency factor
[A]	concentration of A
c	concentration
°C	degrees Celsius
C_p	heat capacity at constant pressure
D(A—B)	bond dissociation energy
$\bar{D}$(A—B)	mean bond dissociation energy
e	electronic charge; exponential
E	activation energy; electromotive force; Coulomb energy
E(A—B)	bond energy
F	Faraday
g	gas
G	free energy
h	Planck's constant
H	enthalpy or heat content
k	Boltzmann constant; specific reaction rate
k_2	specific reaction rate
K	equilibrium constant
°K	degrees Kelvin (absolute)
l	liquid, litre
ln	logarithm to base e
log	logarithm to base 10
M	Madelung constant
N	Avogadro number
p	partial pressure
P	total pressure
r	interionic distance
R	gas constant
s	solid
S	entropy

t	time
T	temperature
U_0	lattice energy
V	volume
z	number of charges on ion
Δ	change in

Subscripts

f	formation
298	298°K
eq	per equivalent

Superscripts

0	standard
a	from the atoms
‡	activated

Examples of composite symbols

ΔG^0_{298}	standard free energy change at 298°K
ΔH^0_{f298}	standard enthalpy (or heat) of formation at 298°K
$\Delta S^{0‡}_{400}$	standard entropy of activation at 400°K

INDEX

action constant 108
activated complex 109
activation energy 108
  and enthalpy change 109
  as energy barrier 110
  in exothermic and endothermic reactions 110
Arrhenius equation 108

Boltzmann constant 113
bond dissociation energy 86, 96
  mean 97
  of hydrogen, halogens, and hydrogen halides 97
  relation to bond energy 97
bond energy
  in polyatomic molecules 94
  of C—H and C—C in alkanes 93
  single 92
  sum 92
  use in assessing potential structures 93
Born-Haber cycle 79

catalysis, energetic approach to 98
  limitation of 105
catalyst, function of 98
Clausius-Clapeyron equation 42
Conservation of Energy, Law of 43
Conservation of Mass, Law of 6
covalent bonds
  and electronegativity difference 87
  in diatomic molecules 85
  in polyatomic molecules 88
  normal 85
  partial ionic character 88

Deacon process
  catalyst and proposed reaction scheme 99
  energetic assessment of oxide-chloride pairs 101–4

electrochemical cell 54
electrode potential 56
  standard 57
electromotive force 54
  and free energy change 55
  standard 55
electron affinity 82
  and electronegativity 87
  in Born-Haber cycle 79
  of halogens 84
Ellingham diagrams 76
energy
  and chemical bonding 78
  and ionic equilibria 51
  and periodic table 62
  definition 19
  lattice—see *lattice energy*
  total, free, fixed or organizational 18
enthalpy and enthalpy change 20
  as function of temperature 22
  in Born-Haber cycle 80
  in formation of ions 49
  in hydrate formation 47
  in ionic reactions in solution 60
  in physical equilibria 39
  of activation 114
  of solution 45
  standard of formation of elements and compounds 25
  standard of formation of solutes in aqueous solution 48

INDEX

entropy and entropy change 20
  and disorder 29
  and heat capacity 27
  and organizational energy 20
  in ionic reactions in solution 60
  in physical equilibria 39
  of activation 114, 115
  standard of elements and compounds 28
  standard of solid elements 63
  standard of transition series 65
equilibria
  and reversibility 3
  static and dynamic 4
  time invariance 2
equilibrium constant 5
  and extent of reaction 15
  and standard free energy change 15
  combination of 13
  condensed states 9
  convention 5
  relationship between K_p and K_c
equilibrium state 4, 24
extensive properties 14

free energy and free energy change 18
  and electrode potentials 55
  and Ellingham diagrams 76
  and extent of reaction 15
  calculation of 30
  in physical equilibria 39
  of activation 114
  of oxides of first transition series 73
  spectra 68–71
  standard and electromotive force 53
  standard and equilibrium constants 14
frequency factor 108

heat capacity 21
  and entropy 27
  as a function of temperature 22
  at constant pressure and volume 21
  in influence of temperature and equilibria 34, 36
  standard of elements and compounds 38
heat content 20
  (see also *enthalpy*)

heat of combustion 85
  and heat of formation of organic compounds 89
heat of dilution, integral 46
heat of formation of elements and compounds 23
  standard 24
heat of neutralization 49, 52
  in relation to acid-base strengths 48
heat of solution, integral 46
heat of vaporization 39

intensive properties 21
ionic product for water 52
  variation with temperature 52
ionization energy 82
  and electronegativity 87
  first of elements 84
  in Born-Haber cycle 79
  successive for elements H to Na, 84

lattice energy
  for ionic solids 79
  from Born-Haber cycle 79
  from models 81
laws of thermodynamics 42
  and Hess's law 43
  Second Law 42
  Second Law manifestations 44
  Third Law 43

Madelung constant 81
models in chemical bonding 78

Nernst equation 56

overall order of reaction 107

Planck's constant 113

rate constant 108
rate of chemical reaction 107
reactants and products in chemical reactions 5
reaction coordinate 109

solubility product 58
specific reaction rate 108